Mammals

Mammals

CONTENTS

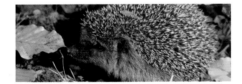

GRASSLAND

Grassland accounts for more than 25 per cent of the earth's vegetation zones. Uninterrupted, open landscapes of this kind are characterised by an absence of trees and are dominated by grasses, a type of vegetation so undemanding that it has only one requirement – light. Grasses will not grow in places where there is insufficient light. They will, on the other hand, withstand drought and floods, blistering sun and periodic fires and can even survive the teeth of millions of hungry animals since their roots remain undamaged beneath the ground. Grassland areas are known by different names depending on their geographic position.

How does the field hare give its enemies the slip?

If a hare crouching flat on the ground detects an approaching predator, it will suddenly leap up and race off at speeds of up to 80 kilometres per hour. Water and fences pose no obstacle as hares are good swimmers and climbers. The hare will also confuse its enemy by zigzagging – quickly changing direction at speed.

What is a 'form'?

This is the name given to the hare's nest, a shallow depression which it hollows out of the ground. The hare crouches down flat in its form, the colour of its fur providing such good camouflage that its back is barely visible. It usually lies with its nose into the wind so that it can scent any approaching predator.

What does the hare feed on?

A hare's diet includes grasses, herbs, fruit, mushrooms, new buds and roots although it may also eat small animals and carrion. In winter it strips the bark and bast (fibrous material) from shrubs and trees.

What is the difference between hares and rabbits?

Whilst the hare is a solitary creature living above ground, rabbits construct elaborate underground burrows where they live in social groups. Hares are also considerably larger than rabbits and have longer ears and legs.

Sitting up on its hind legs, the hare keeps a lookout for enemies.

Whilst some rabbits remain on the lookout for danger, the rest of the group can feed in peace.

Rabbits are not solitary creatures but prefer to live in large groups in a warren. They have a great deal of body contact with one another and even the underground burrows are occupied by several rabbits at a time. A strict hierarchy exists among the members of a warren.

Why are rabbits described as social animals?

Mole rats are rodents which, like moles, live underground where they have no need of eyes. Consequently, the mole's tiny eyes are the size of a poppy seed hidden beneath the skin. These creatures find their way around using a strip of whitish sensory bristles extending from the nose to the eyes.

Is a blind mole rat really blind?

The wood mouse's main predators include foxes, martens and owls. If the mouse spots an approaching enemy in time it will often escape by means of a series of long hops, using just its hind legs.

Why are wood mice also known as jumping mice?

The distribution area of mound-building or Steppe mice extends from Southeast Europe to the Volga. In Central Europe, for example, they can be found around Lake Neusiedler. Their elaborate system of burrows includes several tunnels leading upwards to a food chamber, which resembles a molehill from the outside. The mound-building mouse gathers stores for the winter, usually bitten off ears of grain, which it piles into mounds and covers with a layer of earth. Some stores have been found to contain up to ten kilograms of grain.

What are the nesting habits of the mound-building mouse?

The striped field mouse has reddish-brown fur with light-coloured underparts. A dark stripe resembling a branding mark runs the length of its spine. Striped field mice are true mice with large eyes and ears and long tails.

Why is the striped field mouse so named?

What are root voles?

These are small rodents with stocky little bodies, a short tail, a blunt, rounded snout and small eyes and ears. They get their name from their tunnelling habit.

Why are field voles unpopular with forestry workers?

Field voles feed mainly on grass stems, seeds, rushes, herbs, roots and, occasionally, carrion. During the winter, however, they will gnaw away at the bark of young trees and bushes, causing them to die. They have been known to cause considerable damage in plantations.

Where does the common vole live?

This is the commonest species of burrowing mouse in Central Europe. Its distribution area extends from Central and Southern Europe to Asia Minor and Central Asia as well as to the Siberian plains in the East. It inhabits fields, meadows, pastures and agricultural land. This small rodent, measuring approximately ten centimetres in length, can be found at altitudes of up to 2,400 metres in alpine regions.

How many young will a female common vole produce?

The female common vole will give birth to between two and ten babies following a gestation period (the time from fertilization to birth) of 20 days. Depending on the amount of food available, she can become pregnant from three to six times a year. The young are able to look after themselves when they are just three weeks old and young females can become pregnant themselves at just 12 days old. Adding together the potential number of children, grandchildren, great-grandchildren etc., a field mouse can produce around 1,000 offspring within one year.

How do wood mice tracks differ from those of a common vole?

When crossing snow, mice leave the tracks of their paws behind. In the case of a wood mouse, which belongs to the class of true mice or long-tailed mice, the tracks include a fine groove made by its long tail. Voles, on the other hand, have shorter tails, which only leave a trail in deep powder snow.

Voles often live in large groups, occupying an elaborate system of shallow burrows constructed just beneath the ground.

With the exception of the muskrat, which was introduced from North America, the water vole is the largest European vole.

The common vole is subject to population explosions of a cyclical nature. Every three to four years there is a dramatic increase in the number of common voles. Soon afterwards the population begins to decline due to food shortages, stress and an increase in the number of predators. The vole population then increases again over the next three to four years. For many predators, common voles form almost 90 per cent of their diet. Their numbers rise and fall along with the voles.

Rearing up on its hind legs, the hamster displays its dark belly.

What are the habits of the water vole?

Water voles are very adaptable and, depending on their habitat, occur in two different forms: a burrowing species (found in Central Europe) which lives in dry habitat, and a species which makes its home near water. The burrowing species constructs an elaborate underground system of burrows whilst the more familiar aquatic species is a good swimmer and able to dive. The two forms can be distinguished by their upper molars: the species that lives near water has teeth that are vertical and do not point forwards.

What is the difference between a mole-hill and the mound made by a water vole?

The mole excavates its burrows by pushing the earth vertically upwards with its head and paws, thereby creating a molehill. There is never an entrance hole to the burrow anywhere near the mound. Mounds created by water voles, on the other hand, are usually flatter and longer, and the soil will be mixed with grass. The entrance to the burrow will be situated next to the mound.

How does the European hamster react to danger?

Measuring just 30 centimetres from head to tail, the European or black-bellied field hamster is nevertheless adept at protecting itself. When threatened by a predator, such as a buzzard, it will stands on its hind legs and puffs out its cheek pouches, making itself appear larger. It will also snarl and hiss aggressively. When cornered, the hamster will bite its enemy using its chisel-shaped teeth, which can inflict considerable damage.

Why does the European hamster have a dark belly?

Most mammals have underparts which are either lighter than or the same colour as their upper parts. The European hamster is different in this respect. With its reddish-grey or greyish-brown fur, it is almost invisible to an airborne predator. Standing upright and displaying its dark belly to a potential attacker is frequently deterrent enough to cause most predators to hesitate. The hamster can then use this breathing space to escape.

Which mouse is the most accomplished architect?

The harvest mouse attaches its beautiful spherical nest to the stems of reeds, long grasses or cereal crops up to one metre above the ground. It does so by shredding the leaves of the host stems into thin strips and weaving them into a ball-shaped framework. Since the leaves are left attached to the host plant, the colour of the nest is green to begin with. Breeding nests have just one entrance hole whereas non-breeding nests have two.

How has the harvest mouse become adapted for climbing?

Harvest mice are generally to be found living amongst tall-stemmed grasses, reeds or rushes in damp meadows. Their prehensile tails are a useful aid when they are climbing amongst this sea of grasses in search of food, for example. When descending, they can hook the tail around the stem for additional grip.

How does the mole move about underground?

The mole has developed broad shovel-like front feet, with which it propels itself forward using backward strokes, in a manner similar to a swimmer's breaststroke. Since its fur does not lie in one particular direction, it can crawl forwards as well as backwards through its tunnels.

The harvest mouse, Europe's smallest rodent, sometimes makes its nest in fields of cereal crops.

Shrews, such as the common shrew, have a long pointed snout consisting of an upper lip and nose. Its mouth is found on the underside of this trunk-like snout. It has forward-pointing incisors, which act like pincers.

What is a shrew?

The European ground squirrel or European souslik hibernates during the winter in its burrow, which can be up to one and a half metres below the ground. Having first made itself a cosy nest out of grass, it seals up the entrance to the burrow with earth. During hibernation, the squirrels exist on about 130 grams of stored fat, which they build up during the summer. They do not lay down stores of food.

What do European ground squirrels do in winter?

Meadow jumping mice have long hind feet, which enable them to move forward in leaps. Although they normally use all four feet, if they find themselves under attack or forced to cross a large exposed area without any protective cover, they can leap up to a metre at a time using only their hind legs. The long tail also helps jumping mice to retain their balance.

How do meadow jumping mice escape from predators?

Shrews frequently consume more than their own body weight of food each day. They are unable to survive for more than a few hours without food.

The European ground squirrel is related to the marmot. Like marmots, they have sentries that whistle loudly to warn their neighbours of danger.

How does the European polecat deter predators?

When threatened by a predator, such as a fox or an owl, the polecat repels its opponent by secreting a strong-smelling fluid from its anal glands. It also marks its territory in this way.

Which predatory mammal is small enough to fit through a wedding ring?

In its search for prey, the pygmy weasel, which feeds mostly on mice and voles, is able to penetrate the homes of even the tiniest burrowing animals. The pygmy weasel is the smallest of any living predatory mammal.

Why do stoats run so fast?

In pursuit of their prey, stoats can reach speeds of up to 30 kilometres per hour, which equates to 100 metres in 12 seconds. These mammals have extremely flexible spines, a physical characteristic which enables them to leap up to one metre in the air from a standing position.

How does a skunk defend itself?

If threatened, a skunk will present its hindquarters to its enemy, raise its tail and spray an extremely offensive smelling fluid into its opponent's face. Quite apart from the smell, skunk musk can also cause temporary blindness if sprayed in the victim's eyes.

The nocturnal polecat scent-marks its territory, which can extend over several square kilometres.

The Chinese water deer is the only deer without antlers.

The skunk's defence is a chemical weapon: a foul smelling secretion produced by its anal glands.

Why do skunks have such striking colouring?

A skunk's black and white striped fur and bushy tail warn potential predators that it knows how to defend itself.

Which species of deer does not have antlers?

Even the male Chinese water deer lacks antlers. Instead, the buck develops long canine teeth that protrude from the upper jaw as tusks and remain visible even when the mouth is closed. The species is native to northeastern parts of China and Korea. They were introduced to a park in the south of England and several escaped into the wild.

The curved, downward-pointing canine teeth protrude up to eight centimetres from the water deer's mouth. They are dangerous weapons which the bucks use mainly in aggressive encounters with rivals. Bucks are highly territorial and will only tolerate females in their vicinity. Any rival will be immediately chased away. In any confrontation, each male will try to stab the other in the head or on the neck with downward thrusts of its head. These fights often produce deep, bloody wounds. The defeated buck submits by laying his head and neck flat on the ground.

Stoats or ermine mate in late spring between April and July. The young are not born for another ten months. This unusually long gestation period is due to the fact that there is a period of delay before the egg is implanted in the uterus and gestation begins.

What does the Chinese water deer use its tusks for?

What is delayed implantation?

How many vertebrae are in a giraffe's neck?

At five metres in height giraffes are the tallest mammals on earth. Their necks alone measure about two metres in length. The giraffe, like any other mammal, still has just seven neck vertebrae, although each one is greatly elongated.

Is the giraffe a precocial mammal?

A precocial animal is one that is born relatively well developed and capable of running with its mother and the rest of the herd very soon after birth. A baby giraffe falls into this category: just 20 minutes after being born, it is able to stand and an hour later will suckle from its mother.

How do zebra stallions fight?

Fights between rival male zebras begin with the males circling each other, trying to bite their opponent's legs. To avoid being bitten, zebras will drop to their knees or roll around on the ground. This 'aggressive circling' behaviour may be followed by a neck contest, in which each male tries to force its rival's neck down. The fight then escalates to both animals rearing up and attacking each other with their front hooves and teeth. The winner is the zebra that causes its adversary to lose its balance.

To avoid being in competition over food, zebras, gnus and gazelles all eat different types of plants.

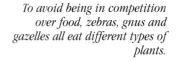

Although they occupy the same habitat, these animals coexist quite happily because they do not eat the same plants. Zebras, like all horses, have upper and lower teeth so they can tackle tough grasses. Once the grasses have been grazed, the gnus can nibble at the leafy plants lying beneath. The tender shoots emerging from the ground are food for the small gazelles.

Why are zebras, gnus and gazelles not in competition with one another?

Some male reedbucks and water antelope, as well as grazing antelope, occupy small mating sites, known as 'arenas', to which they have previously laid claim in ritualised, bloodless combat. The females wander through these mating arenas, are courted by the individual occupiers and eventually mate with a buck after an elaborate courtship ritual.

Which antelope performs a courtship display?

The moment gazelles spot a predator, they perform a high, bounding leap, propelling themselves into the air with all four legs stiff and straight. It is thought that this behaviour acts as a warning to the rest of the herd and signals to the enemy that they have been discovered. It also indicates that the gazelles are far too fit to be the target of a potential attack.

Why do Thomson's gazelles leap vertically into the air?

Zebras are known for their distinctive black and white stripes. No two animals are alike and zebras recognise each other from their individual patterns.

The giraffe's long neck ensures that it has no need to compete with other herbivores (plant eaters) for food since it feeds on the tender leaves of tall acacia trees.

Why do gnus migrate?

Gnus generally live in areas where the grasses are short and grow with the rhythm of the rainy and dry seasons. Gnus are constantly on the move, therefore, migrating to areas of recent rainfall where fresh grass is sprouting. In doing so, they often form huge herds. When crossing rivers, gnus sometimes panic, in which case hundreds can drown or be trampled to death.

How do herbivores digest plants?

All herbivores, such as hoofed animals, require the assistance of bacteria to digest their food. Bacteria break down the cellulose from the plant cells into smaller components, which the animals are able to digest more easily. In the case of ruminants (animals that chew the cud), such as cattle, antelopes and deer, the bacteria live in the rumen and reticulum compartments of the stomach.

How do eland differ from other bush antelope?

Unlike other bush antelope, such as the Greater Kudu, both male and female eland (as well as the Bongo antelope) have horns. The females use them to defend their calves; several females may join forces to put a cheetah or leopard to flight.

Impalas are territorial animals. The leader of the herd will drive out a rival from its territory in a wild chase.

Many species of antelope migrate to wherever there is fresh grass, following the food supply.

During the dry season, gnus are sometimes obliged to walk 50 kilometres to find a waterhole.

They often do so for many hours on end, remaining virtually motionless. This is how the animals doze. The additional height gives them a good all-round viewing position from which they can monitor the surrounding area. It is also a means whereby the bull antelope can signal his claim to a particular territory. It is believed that the animals may also be seeking the relief of cooler air found on this higher ground.

Why do Hunter's antelope stand on termite hills?

The antelope bull leaves droppings along the boundaries of its territory. It also marks the ground with secretions from its preorbital scent glands by dropping to its knees and rubbing its horns in damp earth.

How does a male Hunter's antelope mark its territory?

Female sable antelopes live in smaller groups with their young, led by a strong male antelope. He keeps watch over the grazing herd. If the leader spots potential danger in the vicinity, he will confront the predator, usually with the help of two or three other young bucks. This strategy allows time for the rest of the herd to escape.

How does the sable antelope defend itself?

At the start of the mating season, a territorial buck will gather a group of females around him. He can tell from the scent of a female's urine whether or not she is in season. If she is, he will start harassing her before following her in a mating march, whereby the male walks some distance behind her, constantly tasting the air with his tongue. If the doe is ready to mate, she will allow the buck to approach and lick her back, before he mounts her.

How do impalas mate?

Impalas are also known as 'black-heeled antelope' due to the clump of black hair just above their heel. This distinctive mark is particularly noticeable when the animals are taking bounding leaps as they flee from a predator. Glands produce a scent during flight, which is picked up by the rest of the herd.

How does the impala get its alternative name?

How does the elephant use its trunk?

The elephant's long, muscular trunk is the equivalent of a human nose. These grey giants use it to trumpet, breathe, smell and pick up food such as clumps of grass or leaves, which they then transfer to their mouth. They also use their trunks to lash out at their enemies during a confrontation.

How do elephants keep in touch over long distances?

Elephants can communicate across great distances (100 kilometres). They do so not by the loud trumpeting normally associated with elephants but by means of low-frequency sound (infrasound), which humans cannot hear.

Why do African elephants have such big ears?

An elephant's ears not only enable it to hear but also serve as a cooling device. When the animal becomes too warm, it flaps its ears to create a breeze and rids itself of body heat over a large surface area. Also, a charging bull elephant will spread its ears wide to appear more intimidating.

A drinking elephant can draw up 15 litres of water with its trunk in one go.

What does an aardvark eat?

An aardvark's diet includes insects, such as grasshoppers, ants, beetles and their larvae, but its favourite prey are termites. Strong claws on its front feet enable it to break open a termite hill allowing it to scoop up the termites with its 30-centimetre long tongue. The aardvark produces large quantities of sticky spittle to ensure that the termites stick to its tongue.

How does an aardvark defend itself?

If threatened, the aardvark will try to escape by quickly digging itself into the ground. It loosens the ground with its powerful claws at incredible speed, pushing it backwards to its hind legs that in turn kick the soil behind the animal. The aardvark literally sinks into the ground in a matter of seconds. If it fails to make its escape quickly enough, it will roll onto its back and turn its sharp claws towards its attacker.

The broad horns of a fully-grown bull buffalo can span over a metre in width.

All species of the rhinoceros family are endangered due to the fact that rhinoceros horn is reputed to have aphrodisiac powers, that is to say, it is said to increase the sex drive in humans. For this purpose, its powdered form is used primarily in Chinese medicine. Exhaustive studies have proven that this notion is based purely on myth, one which is nonetheless leading to the extinction of the species. Like human fingernails and hair, the horns consist of keratin.

The aardvark will break open a termite hill to get at its favourite delicacy, scooping the termites up with its tongue as they seek to escape.

In addition to swishing their tails and twitching their muscles in places where insects land on their skin, buffalo also enjoy wallowing in mud. The insects are then unable to penetrate the crust formed by the dried mud. Buffalo can often be seen rubbing themselves against tree trunks or termite hills. They also have a cooperative relationship with certain birds, such as buffalo birds and cattle egrets, which pick the parasites off their hide.

How do African buffalo repel insects?

As well as adopting certain body stances and various head movements, buffalo also communicate by using various vocal signals. Specific vocal communication has been documented between the cows and their calves as well as between individual members of the herd. In addition, specific vocal signals can be distinguished during rutting and mating, as well as special calls used as warning or aggressive signals.

How do buffalo communicate with each other?

The white or square-lipped rhinoceros of the Savannah is larger than the forest-dwelling black rhino and has more pronounced humps on its neck. Both species have two horns on their nose. Whereas the black rhino's upper lip comes to a point and can be used to grasp things, the white rhino has a wide square lower and upper lip.

What is the difference between the two species of African rhinoceros?

Using its broad mouth, the white rhino tightly clamps its lips around a clump of grass and tears it up.

How does the white rhino feed?

The armadillo's armour-like skin is its main protection against predators. The armour consists of plates of bone with an additional covering of horn. When danger threatens, some species tuck their legs beneath their armour and press themselves into the ground. Other species roll themselves up into a ball.

Which animal wears a suit of armour?

What is the function of the warthog's 'warts'?

Warthogs have three pairs of warts on their face: one pair near the eyes, one on the snout and one on the lower jaw. The ones near the eyes are the smallest and are not even present in some females. On a boar, the warts on the snout can grow to 15 centimetres. In both males and females, the warts on the lower jaw are surrounded by white bristles and resemble tusks in the case of young males. It is believed that these warts protect the eyes and lower jaw when the animals fight.

How does the warthog protect itself from predators?

A warthog's eyes are located relatively high on its head giving the animal a good view of its surroundings even whilst it is kneeling down and shuffling along on its knees to feed. If a predator is too powerful and the warthog has to make a run for it, it is capable of speeds of up to 55 kilometres per hour. When warthogs run, they stick their tails in the air as a warning signal to others that danger is near.

How does the warthog defend itself against enemies?

If threatened by an enemy, such as a leopard, a warthog will try to ward off its opponent using its sharp tusks, which are capable of inflicting serious injury. It will also use its tusks in confrontations with rival males.

A warthog's tusks are dangerous weapons. Both pairs of teeth in the lower and upper jaw grow upwards.

Most cats are solitary animals that prefer to hunt alone. The lion is the only big cat to live in a family group, known as a pride. The females generally hunt together, following a specific hunting technique. They creep as close as possible to a herd of zebras, for example, then one female will circle the herd and show herself, throwing the animals into a panic, causing them to flee towards her waiting companions. As soon as a zebra crosses her path, the lioness strikes.

How do the hunting methods of lions differ from those of other big cats?

The sooner a cub is dead, the sooner its mother will be ready to conceive again and mate with the new male. In this way, the new pride leader ensures that it is his genes that are passed on to the next generation.

Why does a male lion kill all the young cubs when it takes over a new pride?

The cheetah is the fastest living mammal. In short bursts it can reach speeds of over 100 kilometres per hour. The cheetah's prey is hares and small antelopes. Speed is essential for a cheetah since it hunts in open country and must be able to outrun its prey. It is the animal's capacity for speed and excellent hunting skills which compensate for the fact that a cheetah is not as powerful as some other predators, such as lions and hyenas, which often steal the cheetah's kill for themselves.

Why is speed so important for a cheetah?

The lion's regal appearance and skill as a hunter have earned it the title of 'king of the beasts'.

Once the cheetah has brought down a Thomson's gazelle after a high-speed chase, it will often have to contend with lions or hyenas lying in wait to steal the kill.

How do African wild dogs hunt?

African wild dogs usually hunt in packs, setting out on hunting forays in the morning or late afternoon. Having picked out their prey with their excellent eyesight, they then pursue it. When near enough to their chosen quarry, they sink their teeth into its hindquarters and head to slow it down. They then rip open the belly of the animal and tear it to pieces.

Which mammal is the most efficient hunter of the savannah?

Tenacious hyenas pursue their victims until they collapse with exhaustion. They hunt in packs and their technique consists of panicking a herd into stampeding, then isolating one of the animals, usually a youngster, from the rest of the herd. Some members of the pack remain behind the quarry whilst others draw alongside and encircle it. It is then dragged to the ground and killed.

Why does the bat-eared fox occupy a special place within the dog family?

It is the only member of the dog family to depend largely on a diet of insects, consisting primarily of locusts, termites and dung beetles. Its large, wide ears act like ear trumpets helping the animal to locate its prey. They can even pick up the sound of termites moving underground or dung beetles in balls of excrement.

African wild dogs, also known as hyena dogs, do not eat carrion, which is why they are obliged to make regular hunting forays. They can maintain speeds of 55 kilometres per hour over considerable distances.

African green monkeys living in a colony constantly engage in mutual grooming, an activity that strengthens social bonding.

Bush babies are lower primates and, with just two exceptions, are found only in Africa and Madagascar. They can jump a distance of two metres and leap two metres into the air from a standing position.

How did the bush baby get its name?

The animal's round face and big eyes, together with its cries, which sound like the cries of a human baby, may account for the name bush baby.

Why is the bush baby such an agile leaper?

Thanks to their forward-pointing eyes, bush babies have the sort of stereoscopic vision that enables them to ensure a safe landing when performing long leaps. Their long tail even enables them to change direction in mid leap. Fleshy pads on their fingers and toes give the animal additional grip.

Green monkeys are social mammals and live in groups of up to 50 animals. A clear hierarchy exists within the group, which is determined by fierce, but bloodless confrontations. A dominant male emphasises his status by walking around with a stiffly upright tail and displaying his blue scrotum and red penis. If a female or baby is threatened, the male will bare his teeth and move his jaw from side to side.

Anteaters and Cape Pangolins have a diet consisting exclusively of termites and ants. To reach their prey, they break open termite hills using the strong claws on their front feet or dig up the ground in their search for termites and ants, which they gather up on their 20-centimetre long, sticky tongues.

How do green monkeys keep order in the troupe?

Why do anteaters have such long tongues?

Which animal is known as the Indian buffalo?

This name is commonly given to the bison, which 150 years ago roamed the North American plains in vast herds. When Europeans discovered the continent, these animals were hunted almost to extinction. The name 'Indian buffalo' is derived from the fact that the bison formed the basic food source of Native American Indians.

What is the bison's diet?

The species of bison that inhabits the prairies relies on a summer diet consisting primarily of grass, especially buffalo grass, as well as other plant material. Buffalo grass benefits from being grazed and actually thrives better as a result. During the winter, bison feed on mosses, lichen and dried grass, which they find under the snow, using their hooves and head to scrape the snow away.

Which is the fastest mammal in North America?

With an average speed of 40 kilometres per hour, the pronghorn antelope is faster than any North American predator. It can even reach speeds of up to 95 kilometres per hour in short bursts when, for example, it is fleeing from an enemy, but it can only maintain this speed for about two kilometres. It can also jump distances of up to six metres at a time.

The bison's massive head and shoulders are covered in hairs up to 50 centimetres long. Thanks to extensive conservation measures, bison are once again present in large numbers.

When fleeing from danger, the white hairs on the rump patch of the pronghorn stand on end. This white patch is visible several kilometres away and flashes a warning to other members of the herd.

How does the pronghorn antelope signal danger?

The slender body of the black-footed ferret enables it to penetrate the burrows of prairie dog colonies and prey on these rodents in their homes. Prairie dogs are an important part of the ferret's diet but have been hunted so much by man that black-footed ferrets became seriously endangered.

Which animal is one of the prairie dog's most feared predators?

The nocturnal kit fox preys on a range of other creatures. Its large ears help give it excellent hearing which enables it to find its prey. It feeds on small mammals, such as grasshopper mice, ground squirrels and jackrabbits as well as reptiles and insects. It will even eat cactus fruits, grasses and other plant material.

Why does the kit fox have such big ears?

When escaping from predators, the swift fox can run exceptionally fast and also change direction very quickly. The name 'swift fox' speaks for itself. It is one of the fastest predators over short distances of up to 100 metres.

How did the 'swift fox' get its name?

Unlike all other horned animals, the pronghorn antelope sheds its horn sheaths every year – only the stumps of bone remain.

The kit fox is one of the world's smallest foxes. They are much more timid than their relatives and live fairly secluded lives.

What is unusual about the American badger's feeding behaviour?

The American badger preys mainly on small mammals, such as prairie dogs and mice, which it digs out of their burrows. It has sometimes been known to form a working relationship with coyotes, whereby the badger pursues the prey into its underground burrows whilst the coyote lies in wait at the entrance ready to pounce on the prey as it tries to flee. If the badger has caught more prey than it can eat in one go, it will bury the rest for later.

How does the coyote differ from the wolf or fox in its social behaviour?

All three mammals belong to the dog family. Whereas the fox is a solitary animal and the wolf lives in packs, coyotes generally remain with the same female for life. This social behaviour places them somewhere between the fox and the wolf. The pair also hunts together.

What does the coyote's diet consist of?

It is repeatedly claimed that coyotes attack cattle. Their diet in actual fact consists of small mammals and rabbits, the population of which they help to keep down. Occasionally, they will eat fish, frogs or plants. With their taste for carrion, coyotes have assumed the role of public health police.

Despite its name, the highly social prairie dog is not a dog at all but a rodent. Prairie dogs were given their name because of their bark-like call.

The Californian jackrabbit and black-tailed jackrabbit have distinctively large, membranous ears.

Although the coyote is sometimes referred to as the prairie wolf, it is a great deal smaller and weaker than its larger relative.

Prairie dogs live in large colonies comprised of territories belonging to individual families. Their underground system of burrows can span several hectares and, in areas where the soil is soft, extend to depths of five metres. These colonies are known as 'towns' in the USA. The male prairie dog defends the family borders against rival neighbours.

Which mammals occupy underground 'towns'?

Some prairie dogs sit up on their hind legs and monitor the surrounding area. If one of them detects anything suspicious, it will alert its companions with a loud bark-like call. If the threat is a bird of prey, they all immediately disappear into their burrows. Other predators, such as the badger, will be driven off with a pretend attack.

How do prairie dogs defend themselves against enemies?

This rodent has fur-lined pockets or cheek pouches, which open on the sides of its face near the mouth. These can be stuffed full of food to be transported back to the animal's burrow to be hoarded for future use.

Why is the pocket gopher so named?

Pocket gophers build extensive systems of underground tunnels in the deep soil of the prairies. With their round heads and small eyes and ears, their appearance itself is a clear indication of their burrowing habit. They also have powerful feet for digging and sharply curved claws on their forelegs. The sparsely-haired tail is used as a sensory mechanism for when the gopher is moving backwards along its tunnel system.

How have pocket gophers adapted to their subterranean lifestyle?

The Californian jackrabbit's 20-centimetre long ears not only equip it with excellent hearing but also help regulate its body temperature. If the animal is too hot, it lifts its ears and spreads them open so that the breeze can cool them.

What are the functions of the jackrabbit's ears?

How do guanacos settle disputes?

Guanacos are members of the camel family. When agitated, for example during confrontation with a rival, the guanaco will spit, pinning back its ears, lifting its head and sharply ejecting a mixture of air and spittle, which often includes bits of food from its stomach. On other occasions, it will try and bite its opponent on the leg and topple it to the ground. Kicking out with its front legs is another tactic.

Where do guanacos live?

Guacanos are very adaptable and have made themselves at home in a large number of habitats. They occur on open grassland, in shrubby, forested areas and at altitudes ranging from sea level to 4,000 metres – regardless of whether the area is dry, hot, windy or cold.

Why do Pampas deer engage in play fights?

Play fights between male deer are common and are in the nature of training sessions, in which younger bucks challenge more senior members of the herd. After an introductory ritual, they lock horns, pushing and shoving each other back and forth in a struggle for superiority. The loser ends the 'fight' by jumping backwards.

What is a viscachera?

This is the name for the community burrow system, which is home to a colony of viscacha, a relative of the chinchilla. These warrens have been known to assume considerable proportions over the course of time. Up to 50 animals can live in an area covering approximately six square kilometres.

Why are viscachas unpopular with farmers?

The underground warren is made up of numerous tunnels running beneath the surface as well as several entrance and exit holes. If built beneath meadows and pastureland, cattle and people can easily step into a hole and break a leg. What is more, viscachas are herbivores and are consequently in constant competition with cattle for their food.

Guanacos live in small herds of up to 20 animals, consisting of mothers and their calves with a ruling male. Occasionally, males will also form a 'bachelor herd'.

Standing 70 centimetres at the shoulder, Pampas deer are very dainty creatures. Their antlers have just three tines when fully grown.

Camels, dromedaries, lamas and other small South American camel species, such as guanacos and vicuñas, are pad-footed mammals. They have two toes, the splayed remnants of what used to be the third and fourth toes. The other toes have disappeared. The soles of the feet are covered with a tough, yet cushion-like plantar pad. Llamas have narrow pads under their feet, which help them travel over stony ground.

In typical wolf-like fashion, the male wolf criss-crosses its territory on the lookout for small animals, armadillos and plants.

Maras, or Patagonian hares, are related to the guinea pig. They are daytime feeders and will graze whilst remaining constantly on the alert. They also enjoy an occasional sunbathe, adopting a somewhat unusual position for a guinea pig. They lie with their belly flat on the ground and their front legs stretched straight out in front.

How do maras spend their day?

Maras are extremely fast runners and can leap up to two metres at a time – in a manner similar to the gazelle. When fleeing a predator, the mara's 'flash', a patch of white hair on its rump bobs up and down, acting as a communication signal. It is widely visible and alerts its companions, who then join in the flight.

How do fleeing Maras behave?

Tuco-tucos belong to the family of comb rats. They owe their name to the comb-like bristles on their toes, which enable the animal to push aside the soil when excavating an underground burrow.

What is the purpose of the tuco-tuco's comb?

The Pampas fox consumes a varied diet of small mammals, birds, eggs, frogs and reptiles as well as insects and other invertebrates. Occasionally, the fox will catch fish or crustaceans. It also eats carrion and a relatively large amount of plant material.

What does the Pampas fox eat?

Although the maned wolf occupies a shared territory with its mate all year round, interaction only takes place during the breeding season. For the rest of the time they are solitary animals. Before mating, the couple lie close together side by side, constantly licking each other's faces. The invitation to mate comes from the female. The male wolf also helps with the birth by licking the cubs dry and even eating some of the afterbirth. He also involves himself in the rearing of the cubs.

What does the social life of the maned wolf entail?

Which predator is the most widespread in the world?

The cougar or puma once ranged over a territory extending from the forests of Canada in the north, across the prairies and rain forests of Central and South America, down to the pampas of Argentina and as far as Patagonia. Pumas have been hunted to extinction in some regions.

How does a cougar react when angered or provoked?

There are many subspecies of puma extending over a wide range of territory, each differing with regard to physical characteristics and colouring. What they all have in common, however, is long hair on top of their back. When threatened, a cougar can make this hair stand on end like a mane. This makes the animal appear larger, thereby intimidating its opponent.

How does the giant anteater catch its prey?

The giant anteater roams its territory tirelessly – always with its nose to the ground. Its preferred diet is ants, which it digs out of their nests by means of its strong claws. Its long, sticky, tube-like tongue can penetrate the tunnels of ants' nests to catch the insects. The tongue is also barbed to ensure there is no escape for the ants.

Pumas are powerful jumpers and can leap six or seven metres into the air from a standing position. They can also jump from one tree to another.

The giant anteater requires around 30,000 ants or termites per day in order to survive. In the absence of teeth with which to crush the ants' hard protective covering, which is difficult to digest, the anteater must depend on its muscular stomach as well as small stones to aid digestion.

How does the giant anteater process its diet of insects?

When threatened, the armadillo will press itself into a depression in the ground or disappear down a burrow. If there is no place to hide, it will curl up into a perfect ball, thereby protecting its vulnerable underside. Only the powerful jaws of the jaguar are capable of cracking its armoured casing. The jaguar's sharp fangs can penetrate the armadillo's bony plates.

Which is the three-banded armadillo's main predator?

This species of armadillo is a remarkably good runner. If an enemy gets too close, the armadillo will quickly scrape out a shallow hole with its powerful claws to provide protection for its soft belly. Bony plates protect the animal's back. If the enemy remains persistent, the armadillo can literally vanish by digging itself into the ground.

How does the nine-banded armadillo protect itself from enemies?

Giant anteaters always carry their young around on their backs. A natural grasping reflex enables the youngsters to hang on to the hair on the parent's back.

Armadillos, like this nine-banded armadillo, are protected by their chain-mail type armour, which also allows them to forage during the day. The three-banded armadillo has a particularly clever way of defending itself: its defence mechanism is to roll itself into a tightly closed ball.

How do speckled ground squirrel babies develop?

The female of the species gives birth to up to eight young after a gestation period of around 25 days. They open their eyes after 23 days, then one to two days later begin to eat solid food and are able to move around. They are weaned at the age of four to five weeks. Since ground squirrel pups are helpless at birth, they are known as 'altricial' animals.

How does the Syrian or golden hamster protect its territory?

The hamster will warn off a rival by chattering its teeth. If this fails to drive its opponent away, the hamster will stand on its hind legs, puff out its cheeks, hiss and attack. In the ensuing struggle, the two hamsters will try and bite each other. The loser will then quickly withdraw.

If a dwarf hamster spots something suspicious, it will stand on its hind legs and keep a sharp lookout. These appealing little creatures have become popular as domestic pets.

Why do hamsters hoard food?

In the dry steppes of Asia and the Middle East, food is often in short supply, which is why the various species of hamster hoard food – whenever it happens to be available – in their burrows. They have expandable cheek pockets, which they can stuff with seeds to be carried back to the nest. The largest hamster hoard ever found contained 70 kilograms of grain.

The Syrian hamster stores food in its cheek pouches which extend from the mouth right back to the shoulders.

Naked mole rats belong to the family of burrowing rodents and are related to voles and hamsters. They occur in East Asia, in China, Mongolia and Russia.

How does the Siberian dwarf hamster spend the winter?

During the winter, the hamster lives off its substantial hoard of food. Its fur alters to suit the wintry conditions. Not only does it become thicker but also lighter in colour.

How does the Siberian dwarf hamster clean itself?

The hamster arranges its fur so that it lies flat against its body and provides good insulation. To groom itself, the hamster sits up on its hind legs and begins by cleaning its face with its paws, which it repeatedly licks to keep them moist. It then sets to work – by dint of a little contortion – on the rest of its body: belly, back, arms and legs.

How did the grasshopper mouse get its name?

These small mammals get their name not from hopping in grass but from feeding on grasshoppers. Although the name suggests that it belongs to the mouse family, the grasshopper mouse is in fact more closely related to the hamster. There is a northern and a southern species, which inhabit dry, open steppe country from Mexico to southern Canada.

How does the naked mole rat burrow underground?

The naked mole rat inhabits the steppes of eastern Asia. This expert burrower has long, sickle-shaped claws on the three middle toes of its front feet, which it uses to loosen the soil. It can then push the earth aside with its head. Any roots that get in its way can be gnawed in two with its teeth. An experiment carried out on a Chinese naked mole rat demonstrated that when placed on stony ground the mole rat managed to dig itself into the ground within four minutes; after twelve minutes it had excavated a tunnel 70 centimetres long.

What threat do bobak marmots pose to humans?

Bobak or steppe marmots pose no danger to man in themselves. They do, however, harbour fleas and these can carry the bacteria that cause the bubonic plague. Bobak marmots are believed to have served as a host for the bubonic plague epidemic which cost the lives of 60,000 people in the early 20th century.

How is the saiga adapted to life on the steppes?

The saiga antelope is recognisable by its trunk-like, over-sized, flexible nose. The internal structure consists of large air sacs connected by cartilage and is designed to pre-warm cold air in winter and also filter out any dust stirred up by its hooves as it moves about.

What do gemsbok use their horns for?

When several male gemsbok find themselves competing for a female, the rival males will engage in a ritualised fight. The horns are not used as lethal weapons but to determine which animal is the strongest. The bucks begin by locking horns with each other, followed by butting heads. As soon as a buck realises that he is weaker than his opponent, he will turn tail and quickly flee.

Saigas need to drink on a regular basis. Moving along using an energy-saving 'pass gait', that is pushing off with both legs on the same side of the body, the saiga can cover distances of up to 50 kilometres a day without tiring.

This species of gazelle, which inhabits the dry African bush country, has a very long neck, similar to that of a giraffe. It can also stand on its hind legs. This enables it to reach the higher branches of trees, which other gazelles cannot reach.

Why is the gerenuk also known as a giraffe-necked gazelle?

The males of this species have an over-sized larynx which bulges out like a goitre during the breeding season. It also possesses an air sac which can be used as a resonance chamber when emitting vocal calls. The Mongolian gazelle lives on the steppes of Inner Mongolia.

Why does the Mongolian gazelle have a goitre?

Although Przewalski's horse, native to Central Asia, had disappeared from the wild due to man's persecution and the loss of its natural habitat, surviving populations remained in zoos. A careful breeding programme was developed to introduce this horse back into the wild in Mongolia.

Do wild horses still exist?

It serves as a visual signal that she is in season. During the final seven to ten days of this period the female is especially fertile. The leading male of the troop will then mate with her on numerous occasions.

Why does the female baboon have a swollen red rump?

The bobak marmot digs burrows up to three metres deep, which are occupied by families. This mammal is larger than the alpine marmot.

Olive baboons have a complex system of communication. Threatening gestures by a senior male include staring, opening the mouth and emitting a rapid series of grunts.

Which mammal is the original ancestor of the domestic cat?

Domestic cats are believed to have derived from the African wildcat found in steppes and bush-land all over Africa and the Middle East. It preys on small rodents as well as birds and lizards.

Why does the desert fox have such large ears?

Its ears, which are up to six centimetres long, help the desert fox to locate its prey. A skilled hunter, it not only catches mammals bigger than itself, but can also catch birds on the wing.

What do corsac foxes eat?

The corsac or steppe fox lives in the steppes of northeastern China and Mongolia. It preys mainly on hares and rodents, such as marmots, as well as birds, lizards and insects. In winter it grows a thick fur, which has led to its persecution by hunters.

How does the honey badger protect itself against predators?

The sharp claws on its front feet can inflict serious injury on an attacker. The honey badger's skin is also very loose – if an opponent or rival seizes it by the back of the neck, it can, quite literally, swivel round within its own skin and bite its attacker.

The honey badger is aided in its search for honey by a bird called the honeyguide. Its tough pelt protects it against bee stings.

Its dark underside and bandit-like face mask combined with its heavy mottling and dark stripes against a light background give the polecat a striking appearance.

The African wildcat has characteristic markings running into stripes along its flanks. Little is known about its life in the wild.

A relative of the marten family, the honey badger relies on birds to lead it to a source of honey. The honeyguide bird gives a special call to alert the honey badger when it has discovered a bees' nest. The badger breaks into the hive with its powerful claws and feasts on the honey, after which the bird also takes its share. The honey badger's tough pelt protects it from being stung.

How does the honey badger find honey?

The ferret badger lives in the bushland and steppes of Asia. It has adapted to its lifestyle by developing powerful claws on its front feet. Its slender sinuous body and small size enable it to move through burrows. It scents out its prey with its long, very flexible nose.

How has the ferret badger adapted to its way of life?

Although the mongoose or ichneumon is not immune to snake venom, it does have reduced sensitivity to any bites. It can also raise its hair on end to prevent the snake's bite penetrating down to the skin. The mongoose can also remove the poisonous skin of some frogs and toads by rolling the creatures on the ground.

Is the Egyptian mongoose immune to snake bites?

If the mongoose finds an egg that is too big for it to crack with its needle-like teeth, it will keep throwing it backwards, using its hind legs, against a wall or rock until it finally breaks.

How does an Egyptian mongoose break open an egg?

If cornered, the polecat arches its back and raises its tail with the tip pointing towards its head. This makes it seem larger. At the same time it will screech and emit shrill hisses. If this does not deter its opponent, it will spray its attacker with a foul-smelling secretion from its anal glands.

How does the marbled polecat defend itself?

How does the Dorcas gazelle groom itself?

The gazelle nibbles its body with its teeth and lips. It tackles the more difficult to reach places, such as its chest, neck and head with a hoof, by poking a hind leg forward between its forelegs. It also uses its horns to scratch its back.

How do Dorcas gazelles communicate with each other?

In addition to smell, another important means of communication is the visual signal given by the white flash on their rump and tail. A nervous gazelle will draw its tail in, almost completely hiding the white patch. If alarmed, it will raise its tail stiffly in the air so that the white flash is prominent. This warns the rest of the herd to prepare for flight.

How are the feet of the Mendes antelope adapted to sand?

Compared with other antelopes, the Mendes antelope, also known as the Addax antelope, has broad hooves, flat soles and well-developed dewclaws, all of which help spread its weight over a larger surface area and keep it from sinking into the sand.

Dorcas gazelles live in deserts, semi-arid regions and savannahs with sparse vegetation.

How is the behaviour of the Mendes antelope adapted to life in the desert?

When temperatures are high and water is in short supply, these antelope can raise their body temperature to avoid having to sweat. In this way, they save moisture and can often go for months without needing a drink. To protect themselves against the hot sun and drying winds, they spend the day resting in depressions, which they hollow out with their front feet in the shade of rocks.

What does the Arabian oryx's mating ritual involve?

The courtship ritual begins with the pair circling: the bull and cow position themselves alongside each other with their heads and tails parallel and move round in a circle. The circling is punctuated with scuffles, during which they lock horns. Mating is preceded by the bull aiming a kick with his foreleg at the rear legs of the female.

Mendes antelopes do not defend a territory. They detect rainfall with their sophisticated sense of smell and then move towards it.

Mammals have become specially adapted to be able to cope with life in the desert. They can utilise every drop of moisture in their food and, at the same time, the urine they produce is highly concentrated since they pass only a very small amount of water. Desert dwellers avoid the high daytime temperatures by only foraging at dusk or during the night. Many desert mammals have a white belly to reflect the heat given off by the hot sand.

The wild ass may live in separate groups of males and females or sometimes in mixed groups. They move around in their search for food. Some males are territorial and will defend a territory. If a female enters its territory, the resident male will try to mate with her. Any fights that occur are usually between rival males or between reluctant females and stallions. The dominant male will tolerate subordinate males in his territory.

What is the social behaviour of the African wild ass?

The aoudad, or Barbary sheep, is a relative of both the goat and the sheep, and inhabits the arid mountainous regions of North Africa. Aoudads have a mane of long hair on the back of their neck as well as long hair on the throat, chest and knee joints. Excellent jumpers, they can leap two metres into the air from a standing position.

What kind of animal is an aoudad?

Camels and dromedaries have helped man survive in the desert since time immemorial. They are well adapted to desert life. Their humps contain a reservoir of fat.

The camel has almost no subcutaneous fat on its body and loses body heat easily. The two toes are joined by skin that prevents the animal's feet sinking into the sand. They can survive for weeks without water and lose up to a quarter of their body weight during this time. They can withstand a loss of up to 40 per cent of their body's water content, whereas anything over four per cent dehydration would kill a human being. When water is available, a camel can drink up to 100 litres within a short period. They only begin to sweat at temperatures in excess of 40 to 41 °C. At night, their body temperature drops to 34 °C, which means it takes longer for them to warm up the next day.

How are camels adapted to life in the desert?

The obvious difference lies in their appearance: the Bactrian camel has two humps on its back in contrast to the single-humped dromedary. The dromedary also has shorter legs and longer hair which serves the animal well in winter and during the cold night-time temperatures of its desert habitat.

What is the difference between a dromedary and a Bactrian camel?

What is the fennec's most distinctive feature?

The fennec or desert fox has large ears and light-coloured fur – both of which reflect its adaptation to life in the desert. Its over-sized ears help it to regulate its body temperature and get rid of excess heat. Unlike dogs from temperate latitudes, the fennec does not pant, as this would cause it to lose moisture.

Why is the brown hyena also known as a strand wolf?

This species of hyena has two names in English, both of which are derived from its appearance or lifestyle. The long hair around its neck and shoulders resembles a mane or mantle. Whilst the name 'brown hyena' is derived from their predominantly brown-coloured fur, the name 'strand wolf' refers to their habit of foraging for food along the shore, particularly in Southwest Africa.

How do meerkats regulate their body temperature?

When meerkats emerge each morning from their burrows, the first thing they do is sit upright and warm themselves in the sun or lie on their stomachs on warm rocks. Their bellies are only sparsely covered in hair, helping them to absorb and dissipate heat quickly. To cool themselves, they lie down on the ground out of the sun. To minimise loss of body heat during the night, members of the colony snuggle together to sleep.

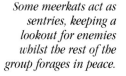

Some meerkats act as sentries, keeping a lookout for enemies whilst the rest of the group forages in peace.

While the rest of the colony forages for food, some meerkats will keep a lookout. If they detect a bird of prey, they emit a long drawn-out warning whistle, a signal for the others to disappear underground. An enemy on the ground, such as a jackal, will be mobbed by a group of meerkats, arching their backs and jumping stiff-legged into the air and hissing and spitting to intimidate.

How do meerkats react towards predators?

During the summer months, the sand cat spends its days in a burrow. When it emerges in the evening to forage for food, long hair on the balls of its feet protect it from the heat of the sand. Its thick fur prevents it getting too cold at night. The sand cat can withstand temperatures ranging from 80 °C in summer to -35 °C in winter.

How has the sand cat adapted to life in the desert?

No, when a porcupine shakes itself, some loose quills may fall out but it cannot shoot them at a specific target. What the porcupine does do, however, is try and ram its quills into the head, neck or chest of its adversary, such as a leopard, should the latter remain undeterred by its initial defence measures, such as raising its quills and shaking its tail to rattle its quills. The quills can inflict serious injury upon an opponent.

Can porcupines shoot their quills at an enemy?

The fennec, a desert-dwelling mammal measuring 20 centimetres at shoulder height, is the smallest fox in the world. In proportion to its body, its ears, which measure over 15 centimetres, are the biggest of any other species of fox.

With its quills raised in a threatening manner, the porcupine can suddenly double its size.

How do gundis groom themselves?

Gundis are a relative of the porcupine. These typical desert dwellers with bodies resembling guinea pigs in appearance have dense, silky fur, which they groom carefully since it provides them with protection from the cold. These mammals have comb-like bristles on the two inner toes of their hind feet, with which they comb their fur.

The sole of a gerbil's foot is covered with a thick layer of hair, which prevents this desert-dwelling mammal from sinking into the sand. Animals that live on solid ground have bare soles.

How does the desert jumping mouse get its name?

Desert jumping mice or jerboas inhabit the arid regions and deserts of North Africa from the Sahara to Arabia. They resemble miniature kangaroos with a long tufted tail. This, together with their long, powerful hind legs, enables them to leap up to three metres at a time. They also use their long tail as a balancing aid. The jerboa's toes are edged with hair to stop them sinking into the sand.

What are the gerbil's feeding habits?

These mammals prefer to forage at night when the dew provides maximum moisture. When they emerge from the burrow, they move very cautiously, their ears constantly alert for any sound since they provide the main diet for numerous predators. Their large ears equip them with excellent hearing – they can even pick up low frequency sounds such as the beating wings of an approaching owl.

Jerboas generally move around on their hind legs. They use their short front legs, which have powerful claws, to excavate their underground burrows.

The springhare excavates an underground system of burrows which it occupies alone. It emerges at night to forage for food.

How do gerbils move around?

Gerbils of the gerbillus species have very powerful hind legs combined with long back feet enabling them to hop along very quickly.

Which mammals have 'midwives'?

The spiny mouse lives mainly in the savannahs of East Africa. In contrast to other species of mice, the young are relatively well developed at birth. Other females help at the birth, licking and cleaning the newborn and – if they are already suckling young of their own – feeding them. The babies gradually become the responsibility of the whole community.

Despite their name, springhares are really members of the rodent family. Recent research indicates that the springhare's closest relative is the flying squirrel even though the squirrel is a tree dweller. The physical differences between the two groups, i.e. the springhare's long legs and the squirrel's gliding membrane, are adaptations to life in their respective habitat. If fleeing from a predator, the springhare's powerful hind legs enable it to jump up to eight metres at a time.

The desert hedgehog lives in the arid regions extending from North Africa to Arabia. It digs a simple burrow up to one metre in length and this becomes its permanent home. It feeds primarily on small vertebrates or invertebrates. Desert hedgehogs hoard food in their burrows. If food becomes short for any length of time, the hedgehog will go into hibernation, during which time it has to rely on its reserves of subcutaneous fat.

Is the springhare a member of the hare family?

How does the desert hedgehog live?

FOREST

Forests are described as the green lungs of the planet. They filter the air, maintain the circulation of moisture, stabilise the climate and provide nourishment for millions of animals. There are several main areas of forestation in the world. The coniferous forests of the northern hemisphere, known as the taiga, are home to far fewer species of animals than the deciduous forests or rainforests. This is because pine trees are not very nutrient rich and they acidify the ground. Further south, the tasty leaves and seeds of deciduous forests provide food for numerous animals. The primordial rainforests encircling the equator contain the highest diversity of species in the world.

When are brown bear cubs born?

After mating in summer, followed by a gestation period of around seven months, the female bear gives birth to her cubs in winter. She withdraws to a den, constructed amongst bushes or beneath rocks or which she has dug out herself. The mother bear usually gives birth to two cubs, which are blind and hairless and no bigger than rats, so that the female is barely aware of the birth. They begin feeding on their mother's milk straight away and remain snug and warm protected by her thick fur. With the arrival of spring, they will follow their mother out of the cave.

What is the most common species of large bear?

Thanks to extensive conservation measures, the North American black bear is the most common bear species. Like the brown bear, American black bears are omnivorous. The fat reserves they build up for the winter derive exclusively from eating berries and plants in the autumn. Black bears, even older ones, are skilled climbers.

Why do wolves howl?

A lone wolf that has lost contact with the rest of its pack will howl to locate the others. They respond to its call by howling in chorus until it finds its way back to the group. Wolves also howl in chorus to strengthen the pack's social bonds and their howling can also serve as a declaration of territory to other wolves.

The largest bears in the world, the North American Kodiak bear and the Kamchatka bear of northern Russia, also belong to the family of brown bears and are classed as subspecies of this group.

The pine marten's throat markings distinguish it in appearance from the similar stone marten. The latter has a forked white marking at the throat whilst the pine marten's throat marking is more cream-coloured and does not fork downwards. The pine marten is also highly prized for its handsome, thick fur.

This large member of the weasel family is a skilled hunter and can sometimes overpower elks and reindeer. Its reputation derives from the animal's original name in Norwegian 'fjellfrås', meaning 'mountain cat', which worked its way into German as 'Vielfraß', meaning 'devours much'.

Why does the wolverine have a reputation as a glutton?

The pine marten, which inhabits large expanses of remote wooded area and preys on small mammals and birds, is the squirrel's chief enemy. It, too, is an accomplished climber and is the only predator that can pursue a squirrel to the top of a tree at speed.

What is the squirrel's most dangerous predator?

The sable's winter coat consists of extremely dense, long and silky fur. It has been greatly prized since the Middle Ages, especially among princes, and even today remains one of the most expensive of all furs. The sable has every need of its warm coat since its habitat is the Siberian taiga where winter temperatures can drop to -50 °C.

Which member of the marten family has the most valuable fur?

The stoat stands on its hind legs and surveys its surroundings for potential prey. Having spotted a rabbit, it will carefully slink forward until it is within a few metres of its prey, before pouncing at the last moment. Even if the rabbit tries to flee, the stoat's sensitive sense of smell enables it to follow and, once it gets within range, it leaps onto the back of its prey, biting it on the back of the neck, which usually kills the rabbit instantly.

How does a stoat hunt a rabbit?

The long-tailed weasel is the North American equivalent of the stoat. Like the stoat, it has populated a large number of habitats. In northern regions, both mammals grow a white winter coat, which provides camouflage in the snow. Only the tip of the tail remains black. The long-tailed weasel is larger than the stoat.

How does the long-tailed weasel differ from the stoat?

Why does the lynx sharpen its claws on tree trunks?

As well as sharpening them, it also helps remove any loosened pieces of nail, ensuring that the lynx's claws remain in perfect condition. Additionally, like all cats, the lynx has scent glands on the balls of its feet and, by scratching at tree trunks, it marks its territory with an odour, thereby proclaiming its rights of occupation.

How does the wildcat differ from the domestic tabby cat?

Despite similarities in appearance, the wild cat is larger and stronger. In addition to its broader head and much thicker, longer fur, it can be distinguished by its shorter, thicker, ring-striped tail which ends in a blunt tip rather than tapering.

How does the musk deer get its name?

The musk deer is the smallest member of the deer family. Instead of antlers the male possesses a pair of tusk-like teeth in its upper jaw, which protrude six to eight centimetres from its mouth. These serve as weapons in contests with rival males. It also has a large gland on its belly, between the scrotum and navel, which produces musk, a secretion with a penetrating odour used to mark its territory and attract females. Musk deer were hunted close to extinction due to the fact that musk was highly prized as a perfume fixative.

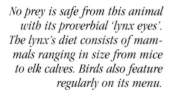

No prey is safe from this animal with its proverbial 'lynx eyes'. The lynx's diet consists of mammals ranging in size from mice to elk calves. Birds also feature regularly on its menu.

The elk, which stands up to two metres in height, is the largest species of deer in the world. Despite its large antlers, the elk is a good swimmer and diver. Its diet includes aquatic plants and it dives up to a depth of five metres to reach plants growing on the beds of lakes and ponds.

Which deer can dive underwater?

The mule deer usually relies on flight to escape from predators. It chooses escape routes that act as an obstacle course to its pursuers. An impressive jumper, the mule deer leaps over small rivers and clumps of bushes, and up steep slopes. It will also stand its ground and defend itself – its agility enabling it to keep out of the way of its attacker.

How does the mule deer react when faced with a predator?

Porcupines defend themselves by charging backwards at a predator and lashing out with their tails in an attempt to ram their barbed quills into their attacker's body. The fisher marten, or pekan, is able to outwit the porcupine by confronting it on the ground and trying to bite it in the face. If the porcupine tries to escape by climbing a tree, the marten will attack from above and continue biting until the porcupine weakens and dies. Only then can the marten begin its meal.

How does the fisher marten overpower a porcupine?

New World porcupines are also known as ursons. They are similar in appearance to Old World porcupines but related to the guinea pig family, occurring only in South and North America.

Wildcats are shy creatures that prefer densely wooded areas. In Central Europe they are only found in a few mountainous regions.

Where does the lively Douglas squirrel make its home?

This typical North American squirrel is also known as a chickaree and is closely related to the red squirrel. It lives mainly in trees, running nimbly up and down the trunks and leaping around in the branches. It descends to the ground either to search for food, to bury food in the ground or to retrieve food hoarded away for the winter.

Where do wood lemmings make their home?

Wood lemmings live on the moss layer on the floor of wet coniferous forests from Scandinavia to Russia and far across to the east. These small herbivores, which are active by both day and night, make their runs and nests in the moss cushion. Wood lemmings, like mountain lemmings, are subject to population fluctuations, although they do not engage in mass migration.

Which two voles spend almost all their life in trees?

Tree and heather voles are found in the Canadian taiga and in the northern USA. They are the only voles to build their round nests in pine trees. Their nests have been discovered as high as 30 metres off the ground although they are usually found between five and ten metres above ground. These voles feed on conifer needles, which have a low nutritional value.

More and more pet shops are selling chipmunks as domestic pets. These attractive little creatures are easily tamed.

The flying squirrel can easily glide across distances of up to 35 metres but, unlike bats, they are incapable of true flight.

Douglas squirrels, like all squirrels, have a role to play as forestry workers – many of the seeds, which they bury and fail to find again, eventually germinate.

Chipmunks sleep through the winter in underground burrows. Before hibernating, they build up a layer of fat from which they draw nourishment during their winter sleep. In addition, they collect seeds, buds, bark, berries and fresh shoots during the summer months, filling their ample cheek pouches with food which they stockpile in storage chambers in their burrows. If they awake in winter, they eat food from their larder hoard.

How do chipmunks prepare for winter?

The flying squirrel has fur-covered gliding membranes along the sides of its body between its front and hind legs. Its tail is also edged with hair. When jumping from one tree to another, it spreads its legs and glides through the air with the aid of this web of skin called the patagium. The squirrel uses its tail to steer and, by moving its hands and feet, it can adjust the tautness of the membrane, thereby changing direction. Prior to landing, the flying squirrel positions its tail and arms so that it is standing almost vertically in the air. This helps to reduce impact.

How does the flying squirrel 'fly'?

Like our own wood mouse, which it closely resembles in appearance and habit, the white-footed mouse does not hibernate. Under ground it builds a warm globe-shaped nest of grass, foliage, moss and bark, lining it with fur and feathers. White-footed mice spend the day sleeping in their nests and become active at night, when they forage for food, carrying it back to their nest or concealing it with earth nearby.

How do white-footed mice spend the winter?

Bats hibernate in winter, during which time their body temperature drops sharply. Each time they are disturbed, they wake up and their body temperature rises automatically, consuming a great deal of energy. If they are disturbed too often, their reserves of fat will not last until spring when food becomes available once more.

Can bats die if their winter hibernation is interrupted too often?

Which mammal is known as the 'monarch of the forest'?

Since the extinction of the aurochs and bison, the red deer remains the largest surviving wild animal in the forests of Central Europe. During the autumn rut, its continuous roaring can be heard over a considerable distance.

Do red deer injure themselves when they fight?

During the rut, the dominant stag's distinctive roar, which is audible over a great distance, signals his claim to the females in the herd. If challenged by a rival, the two stags will confront each other with lowered heads, lock antlers and push each other back and forth until the loser concedes and runs off, usually without serious injury occurring.

What is North America's most common species of deer?

The white-tailed deer is the deer most commonly found in North America. This deer gets its name from its characteristic white underside, which it displays during flight, raising its relatively long tail like a warning flag in order to signal potential danger to other members of the herd.

What is meant by stags 'rubbing off the velvet'?

Stags lose their antlers every year, growing a completely new set during the winter. As they grow, the antlers are covered with a layer of soft skin, known as 'velvet'. Once the antlers reach full size, the deer gets rid of the velvet by rubbing its antlers against bushes and trees, hence the expression.

How do fawns spend their first few weeks?

Most fawns can stand and take their first steps fairly soon after birth. However, the fawn must remain under cover for several weeks whilst its mother returns at regular intervals to feed it with her milk. The fawn's spotted coat provides excellent camouflage and if danger threatens, it presses itself flat against the ground. The absence of any functioning skin glands make it free of scent and less likely to be detected by predators.

The incisors of a fully-grown wild boar develop into long tusks.

Young red deer and fawns have spotted coats that give them excellent camouflage. They lie hidden in the grass where their mother hides them after birth.

Antlers, such as those seen on roe deer and red deer, are shed each autumn and are then completely re-grown over the winter, enveloped in a thin layer of skin containing a rich supply of blood. When they re-grow, the antlers are usually substantially larger than before. Horns, on the other hand, consist of a core of bone surrounded by a sheath of horn. Horn grows throughout the year and is not renewed. Cattle and goats are two examples of horned mammals.

The antlers are covered by a velvety skin, which provides them with a rich supply of blood during regrowth.

The European fallow deer has been a native of the Mediterranean region since the last Ice Age and was introduced to Great Britain by the Romans. Although wild fallow deer are often still found in Central Europe, especially Germany, they very rarely occur in the wild in their original native habitat. The fallow deer is a very adaptable species and is often kept in country parks and zoos.

Fights break out when male deer compete for access to a group of females. When two rival males confront each other, they begin by walking in parallel until one of the stags rams its head into the flanks of its opponent, which reacts by lowering its head and clashing antlers. They then push and shove each other until the weaker one gives way and retreats.

Since the females do not have antlers, they do not engage in contests of strength but clashes do occur nonetheless. The females will bite or snap at each other. They will also lash out with their front hooves in defence of their fawns.

During the breeding season, the adult males of the species fight bitter battles with their rivals over the females, using their tusks as a weapon. To avoid fatal injury during battle, the male boars develop a thick, gristly tissue beneath the skin on the front of their belly and shoulders to protect them against wounds.

Infant wild boar are called piglets and have stripy coats. When danger threatens, the piglets remain motionless in dense cover, their striped coats providing them with excellent camouflage.

Has the fallow deer always been native to Europe?

What does the fallow deer use its shovel-shaped antlers for?

Do fights also occur between females?

What does the wild boar use its tusks for?

What do wild boar piglets look like?

When was the mouflon introduced to Central Europe?

The mouflon was originally only found in the mountains of Sardinia, Corsica and Cyprus. During the 18th century, the mouflon was introduced into the deciduous and mixed forests of some central mountainous areas of Central Europe and the Lüneburg Heath in Germany, where it is prized among hunters for its fine, curling horns.

What is the name of the European equivalent of the American bison?

The European bison or wisent was once common throughout the forests of Europe. By the early 20th century, wild bison had been hunted to extinction. Breeding programmes in zoos and wild animal parks have saved it from extinction, and a small number of these animals have been successfully reintroduced into the wild in Poland.

What does the Chinese muntjac eat?

This species of deer lives in deciduous woodland with plenty of undergrowth. Its diet is very varied and includes herbs, fruit, grass and leaves, as well as carrion. Muntjac are reported to be skilled hunters capable of killing ground-nesting birds and small mammals by kicking them with their strong front legs or by biting them with their tusk-like canines. This species was introduced into England and is now widespread throughout southern and central England and Wales.

The badger's most distinctive features are the black and white stripes on its face. Despite its placid appearance, it can actually run very fast and is an excellent digger.

The mouflon is the original ancestor of the domestic sheep. During the autumn mating season, the rams perform a ritual courtship around the females, taking part in ritualised fights involving much clashing of horns.

The fox's diet is extremely diverse. Not only does it prey on birds, fish and insects, but it will also eat berries, fruit and fungi in the autumn.

This nickname is given to the large, placid-looking badger. This mammal makes its home in underground burrows, known as 'setts'. The badger excavates the sett using its powerful front legs and their long claws. The same setts are sometimes occupied by several generations of badgers.

Which animal character is known as Brock?

With its pointed features, pert upright ears, bushy tail and reddish-brown fur, the red fox is immediately recognisable to everyone. However, the colour of its fur varies across its vast distribution range, which extends throughout Europe, northern Asia, North Africa and most of North America. Some sub-species have lighter coloured coats, while others, such as the brant fox, have dark grey or even black markings on their belly and shoulders. The cross fox has a dark cross on its back and shoulders. The platinum fox is almost white, whilst silver foxes are predominantly black.

Are all red foxes identical in appearance?

A bird of prey will pluck out each feather by the base of its quill, leaving behind a kink made by its beak. The fox, on the other hand, bites the feathers off so that the lower part of the quill is missing from the feather. Martens and cats tackle feathered prey in much the same way.

Fox or bird of prey – how do we identify the culprit from the way a bird has been plucked?

Is the washing bear or raccoon so named because it washes itself?

No, the raccoon or washing bear was so named because it was observed in captivity 'washing' its food in water before devouring it. In their natural environment, raccoons generally forage for food in water. It is believed that this 'washing' procedure is a substitute for their natural behaviour, which is denied them since captive animals are generally fed on the ground.

How did the raccoon find its way to Germany?

The raccoon is commercially farmed for its fur. During the 1930s, two raccoon pairs were released north of Hesse, followed by further pairs during the Second World War. Since then, raccoons have become widespread throughout Germany, their range extending to the North Sea coast and the Alps. They have also been sighted in Holland and France.

Holding a nut in its front paws, a feeding squirrel will gnaw a little hole in the shell. It then gnaws its way into the nut, splintering the nutshell until it reaches the delicious kernel.

How does the raccoon dog survive the winter?

The raccoon dog is the only member of the dog family to hibernate from November to February. It retreats to a sheltered hole under trees, in the ground or underneath roots. In order to survive the cold season, it builds up its fat reserves in autumn by eating fruits, berries and seeds.

Thanks to their dense, warm fur, raccoon dogs spread in the wild from their original home in eastern Asia to Eastern Europe. They have since spread from there to Central Europe.

Despite its weight, the raccoon is an agile climber and quite at home amongst the branches of trees. Its diet includes invertebrates and small water creatures, as well as fruits and berries.

What is special about the Northern birch mouse?

All rodents have a vertical split in their upper lip exposing the front teeth when they are gnawing. The birch mouse is the only European rodent not to have a harelip.

What is the function of the squirrel's tail?

The squirrel is an expert climber and can run up and even down tree trunks headfirst. Whilst in the treetops, it often leaps from branch to branch and to avoid missing its target, its tail acts as a rudder. Should the squirrel fall during these acrobatics, the tail also acts as a parachute.

The colour of a squirrel's fur is highly variable and can range from very dark brown to a light, reddish brown. There is evidence to link certain colours of fur with specific habitats. Coniferous forests, for example, are more commonly home to dark-coloured squirrels, whereas their reddish-brown cousins seem to prevail in deciduous woodland and city parks. What all squirrels have in common, however, is a light-coloured underside.

Both male and female squirrels are solitary animals and need time to become accustomed to each other before mating takes place. The male chases the female through the treetops, emitting sharp little cries similar to those made by baby squirrels whilst at the same time raising and lowering its bushy tail. If the female is too quick for him, she will stop and allow him to catch up before the chase continues. Eventually she will stand still and allow him to mate with her.

Is the squirrel's colouring influenced by its habitat?

What is the courtship behaviour of the male grey squirrel?

How does the hazel dormouse find its way back to its nest in the dark?

The dormouse's artistically rounded nest made of dried grasses is built in bushes or hedgerows. When night falls, dormice leave the nest to search for food, such as buds, berries, seeds and fresh shoots. Whilst on the move, they repeatedly sprinkle a few drops of urine on the soles of their feet, leaving a scent trail which allows them to find their way safely back to their nest.

How does the 'seven sleeper' get its name?

Nicknamed the 'seven sleeper' because it hibernates for seven months of the year, the edible dormouse digs itself a hole up to a metre below ground as soon as the first frosts arrive in autumn. It rolls itself into a ball, covers its face with its bushy tail and sleeps away the cold winter, when food is in short supply. On reawakening in May or June, it may have been asleep for seven months.

Why are wood mice sometimes called jumping mice?

These nocturnal mammals make up the main diet of predators such as foxes, badgers, and various species of owl. Sitting up on their hind legs with their whiskers twitching on the alert for predators, they can, at the first sign of an enemy, hop quickly away using just their hind legs, jumping 80 centimetres at a time.

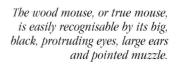

The wood mouse, or true mouse, is easily recognisable by its big, black, protruding eyes, large ears and pointed muzzle.

The edible dormouse or 'sleeper', like the hazel dormouse, garden dormouse and forest dormouse, belongs to the family of Gliridae, a species of rodent known for its long periods of hibernation in winter.

How are baby vesper bats born?

The females of this species give birth to their young in summer, when they are living in hollow trees or nest boxes. When giving birth, the female hangs upside down, extends its tail membrane forward towards its belly, forming a pocket in which to catch the newborn bat pup. Once safely born, the pup will cling to its mother's fur and start to seek out a teat.

How do bats sleep?

During the summer, bats are nocturnal creatures and spend the night hunting flying insects. During the day they roost in hollow trees, caves, attics, buildings or nesting boxes. Hanging upside down by the claws of their hind feet in narrow cracks and crevices, they wrap their 'wings' around their bodies like cloaks.

Which mammal is the most successful North American predator?

Despite competition with other higher mammals, the Virginia opossum has extended its range from South America to Canada. The key to its success is its adaptability. It will eat just about anything and will occupy a wide variety of habitats. It also breeds in large numbers with the female producing up to 18 offspring at a time. Young female opossums are ready to reproduce by the time they are seven months old.

Although the colour of the Virginia opossum's fur can range from white and cream to brown or black, its large, hairless ears, which are folded during sleep, are always dark-coloured.

How does the opossum defend itself?

An opossum will first try to intimidate an adversary by showing its sharp teeth, of which there are 50. If this fails to work, it will pretend to be dead, lying motionless on the ground with its mouth and eyes open and its tongue hanging out, waiting for an opportune moment to flee.

Which gliding mammal holds the record for flying the furthest?

This record is held by the colugo, also misleadingly known as the flying lemur. It has a membrane of skin that extends between its front and hind legs and also runs from its hind legs to its tail. It glides across distances of up to 150 metres.

How did the flying fox get its name?

The head, with its distinctive muzzle, resembles that of a small fox. There are about 170 species throughout Southeast Asia, the Pacific Islands, Africa and Australia. Flying foxes are nocturnal.

Are all bats insectivorous?

No, flying foxes or fruit bats feed on fruits, which they locate with the aid of their sensitive noses and eyes. Their eyesight is even sharper than that of the barn owl. Whereas the latter has 400,000 light sensitive cells per square millimetre in each eye, in the case of flying foxes, scientists have recorded over 670,000 such cells.

The vampire bat belongs to a species of bat with a flat, leaf-shaped nose. Its unusual diet does indeed consist – as its name suggests – of blood.

The Siamang is the largest member of the gibbon family, reaching one metre in height. This mammal spends most of its time in trees.

The mandrill is a rainforest dweller. The male of the species has distinctively colourful facial markings and can grow as large as a St. Bernard dog.

Three species of bat in the tropical regions of Central and South America feed on the blood of warm-blooded vertebrates. They cut the skin of sleeping animals using their razor-sharp teeth, lapping up the blood as it flows from the wound.

Do vampire bats really exist?

This species of bat is found in West Africa and is unique among its kind in its habit of occupying so-called arenas up in the trees where groups of up to 100 males cluster together and make loud vocal calls. This bat got its name from its unusual, square-shaped head.

What is a hammer-headed bat?

Mandrills live in family groups in the rainforest. The facial colouration of adult males is particularly striking. The bridge of the nose and snout is bright red while the cheeks are blue. The blue colouring is caused by protein structures in the mammal's skin refracting sunlight.

Why does the mandrill have a blue muzzle?

Yes, namely the Siamang, a member of the gibbon family, which lives in the rainforests of Sumatra. These mammals live in family groups and mark their sleeping and feeding territories vocally every morning and evening by singing. The male and female sing their duet songs so well together that special listening equipment is required to establish when one of them stops singing and the other begins. Siamangs have hairless throat sacs which inflate with air as the volume of singing increases.

Do singing apes really exist?

White-handed gibbons are social animals, which are active by day. The family group consists of a male and female with their babies and younger offspring. They mark their territory and defend it against rival pairs by singing. White-handed gibbons know their territory intimately and know exactly when each tree is about to bear fruit.

What is the social behaviour of the white-handed gibbon?

How does the spider monkey react when threatened?

As soon as a troop of spider monkeys detects a predator, the males will approach to within ten metres of the intruder, whilst making loud barking calls. They follow this up by vigorously shaking the branches on which they are standing with their hands. Sometimes they will hang by their tails from a branch and shake it with their hands and feet. Spider monkeys also break off branches and throw them at the intruder.

What is the loudest animal in the Amazon?

The howler monkey holds the record for the loudest mammal. Even in the densest forest, its calls can be heard over a distance of one kilometre. They reach such a loud volume by forcing air through their enlarged, hollow vocal chamber. The male's enlarged hyoid bone acts like a resonating chamber so he can call more loudly.

Which New World monkeys are the only ones not to have a long tail?

Uakaris are unusual in having a short, bushy tail. Their bald faces range in colour from pink to bright red, the latter signalling good health. Males attempting to impress a female will scream and perform a dance amongst the branches.

What is the most distinctive feature of the Emperor tamarind?

This lively little South American monkey is distinguished by its long white moustache, which stands out prominently from an otherwise dark face. Its long, rust-red tail also contrasts sharply with its dark fur. The tamarind's toes are not tipped with nails but claws, which is the reason why it is classed as a member of the marmoset family.

How did the colobus monkey get is name?

All African colobus monkeys have a stump instead of an opposable thumb on each hand. The world 'colobus' derives from a Greek word meaning 'mutilated'. The fact that the thumb has disappeared reflects the way the colobus monkey has adapted to its method of travel, which involves moving through the tree canopy, dangling from branches.

Spider monkeys use their prehensile tail as a fifth hand. They use it to dangle from branches, keeping their arms and legs free to feed or seek a fresh handhold.

The diademed monkey lives in the upper levels of the rainforest canopy in West Africa. It will range far and wide in its search for trees bearing ripe fruits.

A major activity among monkeys is what is known as social grooming, which involves the mutual grooming – as a social activity – of another animal's fur on those parts of the body the monkey cannot reach itself. Monkeys use their fingers and teeth for this purpose, meticulously inspecting each individual hair. Mutual grooming serves to get rid of parasites and dirt and is often performed in the interests of relaxing or appeasing a senior member of the troop. It also signals affection.

The guereza is also known as the mantled guereza on account of the white mantle of hair that hangs down from its sides over its black fur.

The guereza's diet consists primarily of leaves. When food is in plentiful supply, the leaves consumed can account for 17 per cent of the animal's body weight after a meal. The guereza's digestive system relies on bacteria to break down the cellulose. Like ruminants, these mammals have a complex stomach divided into compartments, one of which contains the bacteria needed to break down cellulose.

How do guerezas digest their diet of leaves?

This mammal moves through the trees by jumping. Teetering on a branch, it will launch itself headfirst towards a new branch, using its tail for steering. Extending its arms and legs forwards as it jumps, the nilgiri langur lands safely on one of the lower branches in the next tree.

How do Nilgiri langurs cover large distances in trees?

The pig-tailed monkey is a macaque and belongs to the family of guenon monkeys. It derives its name from its short tail that is usually held curled over its hindquarters.

How does the pig-tailed monkey get its name?

Diademed or blue monkeys live in groups of up to 40 individuals, led by an adult male. These territorial animals defend their territory against opponents by emitting low-frequency calls, the sound of which travels a considerable distance through the trees. The male's threatening postures, combined with the calling, is usually enough to avert any further confrontations.

How does the diademed monkey defend its territory?

Diana monkeys live in the upper levels of the rainforest canopy. Each group defends its territory against neighbouring groups. Colourful markings, particularly on their hindquarters, serve to defend their territory. They hang from a branch, displaying the bright orange-red stripe on their thighs whilst simultaneously fixing their eyes on the intruder and staring at it over their stomachs.

How does the Diana monkey threaten its aggressors?

Where do orang-utans live?

Orangutans are found only in Sumatra and Bor-neo and are the best adapted of all the great apes to life in the trees. They rarely descend to earth, preferring to dangle from a branch even when they are drinking. They have opposable thumbs on both their hands and feet, which give them a firm grip when hanging from branches. Their exceptionally long arms are also designed for swinging and climbing through trees.

What does a gorilla's diet con-sist of?

Gorillas are the only primates to feed exclusively on plants, over 100 different species of which provide the leaves, buds, fruit, seeds, shoots and roots that make up a gorilla's diet. Only young or female gorillas feed up in the treetops, as they are light enough to climb to these heights. Male gorillas, weighing up to 200 kilograms, can only watch from below.

What is a silver-back?

This is the name given to the leader of a group of gorillas, a strong, dominant male with a distinc-tive patch of silver-grey fur on his back. Typical features of a silverback are a huge neck and jaw muscles as well as the distinctive crest of hair on the crown and back of the head.

Gorillas are divided into two species: the lowland gorilla, which inhabits the rainforest in altitudes up to 1,500 metres above sea level, and the mountain gorilla, which occurs in regions up to 4,000 metres above sea-level.

These great apes were believed by natives of Southeast Asia to be hairy men of the forest, or, in the Malay language, orangutan.

A distinct hierarchy exists within a group of chimpanzees. The male dominance rank is settled by aggressive posturing, loud drumming with the hands and feet or beating with sticks.

Chimpanzees have developed a wide range of gestures and calls, the most eloquent being their facial expressions. One is used to invite another member of the group to play; another indicates submission towards a senior chimpanzee or supplication. Chimpanzees show they are frightened by opening their mouth slightly and pressing their teeth together. Aggression is signalled when a chimpanzee makes its hair stand on end.

How do chimpanzees communicate with one another?

Chimpanzees are primarily herbivores and their main diet consists of fruit although they do sometimes also eat meat. The males will occasionally hunt and kill small mammals.

What does the chimpanzee's diet consist of?

Bonobos are also called pygmy chimpanzees. The most obvious difference lies in their social structure. Whereas a group of chimpanzees will have a male leader and males within the chimpanzee group will have a higher social rank than females, bonobos are ruled by a matriarch. The males of the group have at best equal status. Bonobos interact with one another much more peacefully than chimpanzees – this is due to the important role of sexual activity which has the effect of decreasing tension and confrontation.

What is the difference between chimpanzees and bonobos?

How have agoutis adapted to life in dense undergrowth?

Evidence of the agoutis' adaptation to their habitat is their wedge-shaped body, which becomes broader and taller towards the hindquarters. The hind legs are longer and stronger than the front legs. To avoid danger, this South American rodent will dive into thick undergrowth to hide.

How tall does a suni antelope grow?

Suni are a very small species of ruminant, measuring at most 38 centimetres high at the shoulder. Only the male of the species has horns, which can be up to 13 centimetres long.

Which deer is a tiger's favourite prey?

The tiger's favourite prey is the sambar, Southern Asia's largest species of deer. Characteristic features include its bristly coat and small mane. It also has a long horse-like tail, a dark brown coat and large antlers.

What is the difference between African and Asian elephants?

Asian, also known as Indian, elephants are smaller animals with smaller ears. They have two bulges on their foreheads, an arched back and smoother skin than the African species. They also only have one finger at the tip of their trunks whereas the African elephant has two.

Asian elephants, like their African cousins, live in herds. Elephant herds can be mixed, consisting of both males and females, or made up entirely of females and their young. Occasionally, male elephants also group together in bachelor herds.

Once the Malayan sun bear has discovered a bees' nest, it will never leave it alone. It uses its long tongue to scoop the bees and their honey from the honeycomb.

The Sumatran rhino's upper lip has evolved into a grasping device which the rhino uses to grab hold of foliage and branches, grasp vines and plants and pick up fruit from the ground.

What is the function of the Asian elephant's tusks?

The elephant's tusks serve both as tools and weapons. It uses them to topple trees so it can reach its branches and leaves, and to dig up roots.

Which mammals belong to the rhinoceros family?

The rhinoceros family includes the Javan and Sumatran rhinoceros, two species which survive in very small numbers in the swampy rainforests of Southeast Asia and the Great Sunda islands. They co-exist in most regions, with the Sumatran rhino more frequently inhabiting mountainous regions, whilst its Javan cousin prefers the open floodplains.

The nocturnal kinkajou lives in the canopy of tall rainforest trees in Central and South America. In its search for sweet fruits and honey, it climbs and leaps through the treetops with the aid of its long tail. Its tail is useful as a climbing aid and to dangle by. It also helps the kinkajou maintain its balance and can be used as a fifth leg. It can hang by its tail as if it were a rope.

The sun bear or honey bear has extremely long claws on all four of its paws, which serve as crampons when it climbs up trees. During the day, it sleeps in the treetops where it also finds the main part of its diet – fruit and shoots. It also catches insects and small vertebrates. To satisfy its sweet tooth, the sun bear uses its claws to rip open bees' nests to get at the honey inside. It will also tear termite hills apart to feast on the insects.

Which bear behaves like a spider monkey?

Why does the sun bear need such sharp claws?

Does the tiger dislike water?

No, the tiger is actually a very good swimmer and diver. In intense heat, it will even spend many hours resting in water. It will follow prey, such as the sambar, into the water and often overpower it there.

How does the clouded leopard live?

Little is known about this cat with its beautiful colouration. It is active at dusk and during the night, spending its days asleep in the treetops. When hunting, the clouded leopard jumps expertly over branches, using its tail as a balancing aid and steering rudder. The clouded leopard and the tree ocelot are the only cats able to climb down trees headfirst.

How do jaguars reproduce?

At mating time, jaguars abandon their solitary existence. Calling loudly, a male jaguar which is ready to mate will try to attract a female. After copulation, the two animals will go their separate ways again. The female rears her young on her own. The newborn cubs are helpless to begin with but open their eyes after just 14 days. They are weaned after five to six months. Young jaguars accompany their mother for a further two years in order to learn to become good hunters.

The tiger's stripes provide it with good camouflage since they break up its outline in high grass or among bushes.

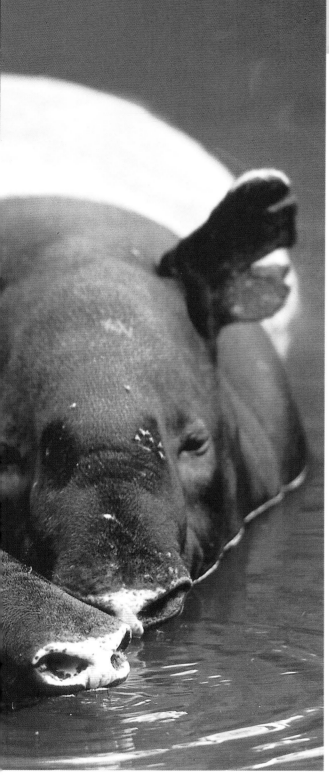

The Malayan tapir has a distinctive light-coloured 'saddle' that contrasts sharply with its otherwise dark fur. This marking appears very prominent when the animal is standing still but provides an effective camouflage for a moving animal.

What is the purpose of the Malayan tapir's distinctive markings?

The tapir's upper lip is elongated to form a short prehensile snout, resembling the trunk of an elephant, and is ideally designed for grasping food and snuffling the ground.

What is the function of the tapir's 'trunk'?

Peccaries have a gland, resembling a navel, which opens on their back. They use the scent from this gland to mark other members of the herd and the boundaries of their territory. The white-lipped peccary does not occupy an individual territory. Instead, it lives in herds of up to 300 animals.

What is the peccary's second 'navel' for?

Sloths spend much of their time hanging upside down from the branches of trees. A sloth's fur is host to algae that colours its coat green and provides excellent camouflage. Evidence of this species' successful adaptation to its upside down existence is the fact that it is the only animal to have hair which forms a parting on its stomach.

How does the sloth camouflage itself?

Tapirs, like zebras and rhinoceroses, are odd-toed ungulates, but whilst zebras have just one toe, tapirs and rhinoceroses have three.

Sloths on the ground achieve a maximum 'speed' of two metres a minute. Since many of the sloth's predators are primed to react to movement, its lack of speed is an effective form of camouflage.

WATER

Almost three quarters of our planet is covered by water. The oceans, which account for an area of approximately 360 million square kilometres and at their deepest point – the Mariana Trench – reach depths in excess of eleven kilometres, provide the earth's biggest single habitat. Even so, this vast area is home to just a few species of mammal. Of these, only whales and dolphins, whose streamlined body shape is – not without good reason – very similar to that of fish, spend all their time in water, as do sea cows. Other mammals, such as sea lions, on the other hand go ashore to breed and moult.

What is the largest mammal on earth?

The blue whale grows to 30 metres in length and can weigh up to 150 tonnes, which is equivalent to the weight of 30 elephants. Even a baby blue whale is seven metres long at birth and weighs between two and three tonnes. Its weight increases at the rate of 100 kilograms each day. After six months of feeding on its mother's rich milk, its weight will have increased more than tenfold.

Where is the blue whale's nose?

The blue whale has a blowhole on the top of its head, which is the equivalent of a nose. It comes to the surface in order to breathe. Once its blowhole is above water, it must first exhale, blowing out a column of spray, before breathing in air.

What is a blow?

This is the name given to the air the whale blows out of the blowhole on the top of its head as it comes up to the surface to breathe. Experts can identify the species of whale from the shape of the blow. For example, the sperm whale's blow is projected forwards at a 45-degree angle, but all other whales blow upwards in a vertical column.

Why do humpbacked whales leap out of the water?

It is believed that the friction created as they emerge from the surface of the water removes irritants, such as barnacles or whale lice, from their skin.

A characteristic feature of the humpbacked whale is the rows of tubercles on the upper and lower jaws, which are often encrusted with barnacles.

Blue whales generally travel the world's oceans either alone, or in groups of two or three. The earth's largest animal feeds on small crustaceans measuring about six centimetres in length.

Male humpbacked whales produce the longest lasting and, tonally speaking, the most complex song of all whales. Their songs have a distinctive structure and a specific sequence of elements, phrases and themes. Research scientists believe that the males sing to attract females. The songs are audible across great distances, some sounds carrying as far as 200 kilometres.

Why do hump-backed whales sing?

This is the white or Beluga whale, which measures up to five metres. The Beluga's songs, consisting of whistles and grunts, are mainly performed during the summer moult.

Which mammal is known as the 'canary of the sea'?

Whales can be divided into two groups: toothed whales and baleen whales. Toothed whales, including dolphins and killer whales, hunt for fish, squid and other marine mammals, such as seals. They have a complete set of small, pointed teeth. Baleen whales, such as the blue or humpbacked whale, filter plankton from the water with the aid of flat horny plates, frayed at the edges, on either side of the upper jaw, known as the baleen.

What do whales feed on?

Probably the narwhal. Its 'tusk' is an extended incisor which projects from the left side of the upper jaw and grows through the upper lip. The right incisor is usually a normal tooth. The spiral-shaped tusk, which is exclusive to the male of the species, has a hollow interior and can grow up to two or three metres in length.

Which mammal is sometimes believed to be the legendary 'unicorn'?

All whale babies are born under water. They are ejected, tail first, from their mother's body. The whale calf has to rise straight to the surface in order to take its first breath. If it shows any reluctance to do so, it is carried to the surface by its mother, or, in the case of some whale species, by other adult females, called 'aunts'.

How are whale babies born?

What are flukes and fins?

The whale's broad, flat tail fin is known as a fluke. It is the equivalent of a fish's tail fin. Its shape is so distinctive that it can be used to identify different species. By lifting their tail fluke into a horizontal position and slapping it up and down, whales and dolphins are able to dive and surface. The fin on the back of whales and dolphins is known as the dorsal fin. In contrast to fish, flukes and fins contain no bone whatsoever but are made up entirely of connective tissue.

Which creature holds the record for the longest mammal migration?

This record is undoubtedly held by the grey whale. They migrate in autumn from the rich feeding grounds around Alaska to the warmer waters off Southern California and Mexico, where they give birth to their young. In spring, they make the return journey to the Polar regions, covering a distance of around 20,000 kilometres.

What do grey whales feed on?

The grey whale is the only species of whale to depend entirely on bottom-dwelling organisms for its diet. Its huge mouth is equipped with baleen plates, covered with coarse hairs, which act like a sieve, retaining the small crustaceans, worms and invertebrates scooped up from the sea bed. Grey whales also strip small creatures from giant kelp.

The male Orca or killer whale has a large, upright dorsal fin.

The sperm whale, measuring approximately 20 metres in length and weighing 45 tonnes, is the largest species of toothed whale. Its large head has a distinctive box-like shape.

Grey whales reach an average of 14 metres in length and can weigh up to 35 tonnes. They do not have fins.

Right whales often breach, in other words, jump right out of the water, slapping the surface with their tail fluke or flippers (the whale's or dolphin's forward extremities which have evolved into fins) as they come back down. They also perform headstands underwater with their tail fins sticking up vertically in the air. The right whale has a smooth underbelly that lacks grooves.

What sort of behaviour is characteristic of the right whale?

In contrast to smooth-skinned whales, of which the right whale is an example, rorqual whales have elastic folds of skin stretching from under the mouth to the belly. These folds of skin play a role in the way this type of whale feeds. They scoop up large quantities of water, pushing it out with their tongue through plates in their mouth. They can do this because their mouths are able to expand dramatically when feeding. Other rorqual whales include the blue whale and humpbacked whale.

The finback whale is a rorqual. What does that mean?

Orcas or killer whales are aggressive predators, which feed not only on fish and squid but, if hunting in groups, will also attack other large whales. They will snatch seals from an ice floe simply by overturning it and sometimes seize sea lions lying along the shore, by suddenly diving ashore, grabbing the sea lion and then allowing the current undertow to pull them back out to sea. The remains of 30 sea lions were once found in the stomach of a dead killer whale.

How does the 'killer whale' get its name?

Sperm whales normally dive to depths of up to 1,200 metres but have reached record depths of 3,000 metres. This was documented when a sperm whale once became ensnared by a deep-sea cable. Sperm whales swimming at these depths hunt giant squid, a fact proven by an examination of their stomach contents. They also feed on bottom-feeding fish and crustaceans.

How deep can a sperm whale dive?

What purpose does the 'melon' serve?

Toothed whales have an organ called a melon on their foreheads. This is a fatty lump of tissue, the shape of which can be altered by special muscles. The precise purpose of the melon is not fully understood but it is believed to help many whales and dolphins locate their position by means of ultrasound. The melon gives the pilot whale a particularly bulbous head.

What kind of dolphin was Flipper, the TV star?

Flipper was a bottlenose dolphin. This species is found worldwide in the coastal waters of warm or moderate seas. The bottlenose also occurs in the North Sea and Mediterranean. Many of the dolphins performing tricks in dolphinariums or marine parks are bottlenose dolphins.

Is it true that dolphins help each other?

Studies of the bottlenose dolphin have shown that dolphins do indeed come to each other's aid. They will support a sick or injured companion and carry it to the water's surface so that it can breathe. They have occasionally been known to save humans who were in danger of drowning.

Pilot whales are easily identifiable at sea by their distinctive, angled fin, which is located far forward on the body.

What is a dolphin's beak?

The group of toothed whales includes some dolphins with an elongated jaw that is known as a snout or beak. Depending on the species, the beak will contain between 100 and 200 teeth. The common dolphin has a particularly broad beak with 40-50 teeth on each side of the upper and lower jaw. The teeth are angled slightly backwards to enable the dolphin to maintain a firm grasp on slippery fish.

What are the distinguishing characteristics of the spinner dolphin?

This species of dolphin is famous for leaping vertically out of the water, spinning longitudinally along its own axis. Compared to other dolphins, the spinner also has a distinctively long beak.

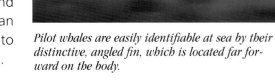

Elephant seals only go ashore to breed or to moult. There are two species of elephant seal: the northern elephant seal, which lives in the northern Pacific, and the southern species, which lives north of the edge of the pack ice in the Antarctic.

Toothed whales use a form of sonar to find their way around in much the same way as bats. They emit a series of clicks, which bounce off objects or other creatures and carry an echo back to the whale. This gives the whale information on its surroundings and the whereabouts of food. Whales can concentrate these click signals in a specific direction. Where and how this occurs is not known, however, and opinions even differ as to how the click sounds are made.

Do dolphins ride the waves?

Many species of dolphin have developed a method of travel known as wave-riding, whereby dolphins are propelled effortlessly forwards like surfers on the bow waves of big ships. Bottlenose dolphins and white striped dolphins also have a reputation for following boats and riding their bow waves.

Do dolphins have to go to school?

Dolphins live in groups called schools. Some species, such as the bottlenose dolphin, form very large schools numbering up to 100 members. The group composition is very fluid – in other words, these social associations are not permanent and the members of a school change constantly.

Despite being excellent divers and swimmers, sea otters are happiest lying on their backs in the water and drifting.

Which seal is found in the Mediterranean?

The Mediterranean monk seal occurs, as its name suggests, in the Mediterranean, especially in the eastern part of the sea. It spends most of its life out at sea, only coming ashore to breed.

Are elephant seals related to elephants?

Elephant seals are water predators. They are members of the Phocidae family, also known as crawling seals, which no longer have rear legs beneath their bodies so cannot move around on land on all four feet. The elephant seal derives its name from the shape of its muzzle. The bull, in particular, has a large, fleshy trunk-shaped and pendulous proboscis, which it inflates and displays during fights with other males during the breeding season.

What marine mammal uses tools?

The sea otter is a member of the weasel family that lives in the sea. It feeds on molluscs, sea urchins and crabs, diving down to collect its prey from the sea floor. It opens hard shells by swimming on its back, placing a rock on its chest and pounding its prey against the rock until the shell splits open.

Which ape has the longest nose?

Unique to the male of the species, the proboscis monkey's large, pendulous nose can reach up to eleven centimetres in length. Since it gets in the way of feeding, the male may have to lift it aside with one hand, using the other to stuff leaves into its mouth. Females and young monkeys of both sexes, on the other hand, have small upturned noses. The proboscis monkey inhabits the mangrove thickets of Borneo.

Which mouse can tolerate salt water?

The salt marsh harvest mouse is one of the few rodents to drink salt water. This species of mouse is endemic to the San Francisco Bay area and is found in salt marshes along the coast. Its beautifully constructed rounded nest is similar to that of the pygmy mouse and is generally found in marsh habitats where glasswort (fleshy plants which grow in coastal areas) abounds.

Which ungulates are purely aquatic mammals?

Sea cows, which, like elephants and hyraxes, belong to the taxonomic group of paenungulata, or 'almost ungulates' are aquatic mammals. There are two species: dugongs, which have a forked tail, and manatees, which have a rounded, paddle-shaped tail. They graze on aquatic plants and algae in coastal tributaries and shallow coastal waters.

The common seal is the most common species of seal and is usually found in coastal waters. Seals are often seen basking on sandbanks.

Proboscis monkeys usually live in trees. They are also good divers and swimmers and may, if threatened, escape by jumping into water.

A young seal pup 'cries' to call its mother if she happens to be away seeking food underwater or if it has lost her (in seal families, the pups are cared for by their mother). The pup's plaintive cries resemble a baby wailing. The National Seal Sanctuary in Cornwall cares for abandoned seal pups each year before releasing them back into the wild.

Which baby mammal wails for its mother?

The common seal is a true or earless seal. It cannot turn its hind flippers downwards and has to wriggle forward on its stomach. The common seal also lacks external ears. Eared seals, such as the sea lion, on the other hand, can use their hind flippers and have the ability to walk on all four flippers on land. Common seals are also more highly specialised for aquatic life than eared seals.

What is the difference between a common seal and a sea lion?

Grey seals, which measure up to two metres in length, are typically found in the coastal waters of the North Atlantic, as well as Europe and America. There is also an isolated population in the Baltic. Thanks to its long head, the grey seal is sometimes also known as the 'horsehead' seal.

Which seals are also known as 'horsehead' seals?

The Californian sea lion, which is popular in zoos and circuses, is probably the best known of all sea lions. The males are much bigger and heavier than the females.

Why does the hippopotamus spend most of its time in water?

The hippopotamus has a very thin skin, which can soon burn and dry out in the hot sun, which is why it spends as much time as possible in water. Its eyes and nostrils are located on the upper part of its head so that it can remain virtually submerged.

Why do hippopotami yawn?

When hippopotami suddenly open their mouths wide in the water, they are not yawning but delivering a warning to an adversary. Threatening posturing of this kind usually occurs during the mating season. In doing so, they are displaying their weapons should the confrontation go any further – huge teeth which can be used to inflict deep wounds on a rival. Threatening gestures are usually sufficient to avert a full-scale fight.

Though not particularly good swimmers, hippopotami make excellent divers and can walk underwater along the river bed. When resting in the water, all that remains visible are their eyes, nose and ears.

Which freshwater seal is descended from a marine species?

The ringed seal is found in Arctic and Subarctic oceans, occurring as far south as the Baltic Sea in Europe. Various sub-species live in freshwater lakes, such as the Saimaa ringed seal, which is found in Finland's Lake Saimaa district, and the Ladoga ringed seal, native to Lake Laloga in Russia. It is believed that ringed seals were trapped in these lakes when the sea retreated from the area and water levels changed. Compared with the Arctic ringed seals, these freshwater species are still fairly primitive.

The Baikal ringed seal, found in Lake Baikal, can dive to depths of up to 300 metres in search of fish. They can remain underwater for 20 minutes at a time.

Despite the strong similarities between the two species, a distinction is made between the European and the American mink.

Which seals live in freshwater?

Baikal seals live in the world's deepest freshwater lake, Lake Baikal in eastern Russia, whilst the Caspian seal lives in the Caspian Sea, the largest freshwater lake on earth.

How does the small-clawed otter eat molluscs?

Asian small-clawed otters seek their food in shallow waters by stirring up the river or lake bed with their sensitive front paws. Having found a mollusc, they carry it to dry land and wait until it opens in the sun. In the meantime, they continue their search for more shellfish and deal with them in the same way.

This species of African otter, which lives south of the Sahara, searches the muddy bottoms of ponds and rivers for crabs, invertebrates and worms, picking up rocks to look for prey underneath. This otter has no claws on its fingers or toes except for occasional small growths resembling human fingernails.

Mink are solitary animals, which defend their territory against rivals. Males and females only get together in the breeding season but rearing the young remains entirely the responsibility of the female. The offspring are self-sufficient by the age of four months when they leave to search out a territory of their own. Mink inhabit dens close to water, which consist of several tunnels, often situated under tree roots. They sometimes take over another rodent's burrow. They catch most of their prey – fish, freshwater crabs, small mammals, water insects and birds – in water.

How did the Cape clawless otter get its name?

What is the social behaviour of minks?

Which mammal works as a landscape architect?

The beaver works on its surroundings until it has created a suitable environment for itself. Beavers will dam a river to make it deep enough for swimming and to prevent it freezing solid. This is an important precaution since the beaver must have access to its underwater hoard of food during the winter. To protect this food store, one entrance to the beaver's lodge must always be located underwater.

How does the beaver fell a tree?

Supported by its tail, the beaver stands against a tree, clasps the trunk in its front paws and gnaws the bark away. It then chisels away at the trunk with its teeth until a deep notch has been cut into the wood, enlarging it top and bottom and on both sides, creating the typical hourglass shape. Once the middle section is thin enough, the tree topples. It takes a beaver just a few minutes to fell a tree with a three-centimetre diameter, but it may have to work for several hours on trees with wider girths.

What does the beaver use its comb claw for?

Beavers have a comb claw on the second toe of each hind foot that they use for grooming their fur, oiling it with a secretion from their castor glands, which are located in pocket-shaped sacs near their tail.

Like beavers, muskrats build dams towering up to a metre in height above the water surface. They build their burrows in steep riverbanks.

The beaver's upper incisors are made of softer material on the inside than on the outside. Since the lower teeth bite against the upper ones, the inside gets worn away faster, leaving the hard outer casing intact and maintaining a sharp cutting edge.

How do beavers sharpen their teeth?

The muskrat is better at swimming and diving than any other member of the vole family. Not only is its fur water-repellent but also the toes of its hind legs are semi-webbed and have a fringe of bristles, increasing resistance in water. Its hind feet serve as paddles and are used in combination with its long, oval rudder-like tail.

How has the muskrat adapted to an aquatic life?

The coypu or swamp beaver is found in shallow waters and wetlands between southern Brazil and Patagonia. Particularly prized for its fur, the coypu, also known as the nutria, is bred on fur farms all over the world, especially in Europe and the USA. Many have escaped from these farms and become feral whilst many more have been deliberately released into the wild. Coypu populations often decline in regions that experience cold winters when the water freezes over.

Where does the coypu make its home?

If a beaver detects a predator, it signals a warning to its companions by slapping the surface of the water with the flat of its tail.

Coypus are similar to muskrats but are much bigger and less agile. Their rounded tail distinguishes them from the beaver.

How does the marsh rice rat behave in water?

Marsh rice rats live along the shores of marshy lakes in southeastern USA. These rodents are skilled swimmers as well as accomplished divers. Their fur barely gets wet in water and an insulating air layer trapped in the hair reduces heat loss. They swim by paddling hard with their hind feet, the layer of air providing additional buoyancy.

Why does the capybara have such a strangely shaped head?

The most striking feature of the capybara is its square-shaped head with eyes, small ears and nostrils all set high up on its skull. The capybara's appearance demonstrates its adaptation to aquatic life: it can stand practically submerged in water, yet still keep a watchful eye upon its surroundings with only the upper part of its body visible. Capybaras also take refuge in water when threatened or in order to cool down.

What is the world's largest rodent?

The capybara is the world's largest rodent. Its habitat ranges from the northern part of South America to northern Argentina and as far west as the Andes. It inhabits lakes and ponds rich in the aquatic vegetation on which it feeds. Its main diet, however, consists of grasses and herbs, rich in protein.

When hunting, the Daubenton's bat emits high-frequency sounds that bounce off its insect prey. It can identify the type of prey from the returning echo.

Like all shrews, the water shrew burns up its energy reserves very quickly and consequently needs to feed continuously. It eats roughly its own body weight in food each day.

The capybara derives its name from a South American Indian word meaning 'lord of the grass', an allusion to its diet of plants.

The water vole makes its home in the densely vegetated banks of rivers, ponds and streams. It is not particularly adapted for a life in water but is an expert swimmer and diver. It is able to eat underwater due to its ability to close off its mouth behind its incisors, thereby preventing water from entering.

How does the water vole eat underwater?

Like all European bats, the Daubenton bat is nocturnal and catches flying insects at night. It flies low over the water, making numerous circular sweeps, and catches insects close to the surface with its tail membrane and hind feet. The bats are sometimes caught by fly fishermen when they mistake the 'flies' for prey.

How does the Daubenton's bat feed?

The water shrew swims and dives extremely well. It has a fringe of stiff hair on the margins of its relatively large hind feet as well as a double row of bristles on the underside of its tail that form a keel and enable it to move quickly through the water. Its thick, well-oiled fur is an effective water-repellent. Its ears, which are concealed in its fur, can be closed for diving.

Is the water shrew well adapted to a life in water?

Water shrews feed on whatever they can find: insects, snails, worms, even small fish and frogs. Out of water they will also eat carrion, which they can detect with their sensitive noses.

What does the water shrew feed on?

A Russian desman is a member of the mole family. These small social mammals are nocturnal. Water is their natural element and they swim by folding their front paws against their body and paddling with their hind feet, using their laterally flattened tail to steer with.

What is a Russian desman?

Why is the sitatunga also known as the marshbuck?

The alternative name reflects the animal's adaptation to an aquatic habitat. Sitatungas feed mainly on aquatic plants and swamp vegetation. Expert swimmers, they rest in water during the day and take to the water to evade predators. They sometimes submerge themselves so that only the tip of the nose remains out of water. Their long, splayed hooves prevent them sinking into boggy ground.

What is South America's biggest deer?

The marsh deer is the largest deer species in South America. It inhabits marshy flood plains and moist forest areas, where it feeds on swamp vegetation. To help it move about easily on boggy ground, it has relatively long, widely splayed hooves, which grow up to 8 centimetres in length. The marsh deer's dewclaws are also quite long, thereby increasing the surface area of the hoof.

How does a waterbuck court a female?

Adult male waterbucks occupy territories in marshy areas around lakes and rivers in Africa, south of the Sahara. They usually occupy these areas all year. When ready to mate, the females of the species visit the bucks in their territories and allow themselves to be courted by the males. The male courts the female by following her around, frequently stopping to lay his chin on her rump or kicking out at her with his forelegs. Bucks will only defend their territory for about three to four years, after which it is likely to be disputed by a younger male.

How does a reedbuck react when threatened by a predator?

The reedbuck's main predators are lions, hyenas and occasionally eagles or giant snakes. The latter are normally only a danger to young animals. When danger threatens, the reedbuck presses itself flat on the ground with its neck outstretched, jumping up at the very last moment and racing away in great leaps and bounds, throwing its hind legs and tail high in the air.

The sitatunga's long fur is oily and water-repellent, demonstrating its adaptation to an aquatic life.

The reedbuck has a fawn-coloured coat. Only the males have lyre-shaped horns which curve forwards and inwards.

Reed- and waterbucks, both of which are found in Africa, not only make their homes close to water, but also spend a good deal of time in water. Their shaggy coats are largely water-repellent thanks to oily secretions from their sweat glands. Territories are rated not by the availability of food supply but by the territory's accessibility to water. This likewise governs the size of individual territories since a superior region will be occupied by a large number of these mammals.

The crab-eating raccoon is a species of raccoon native to marshy and jungle areas of South America. It feeds mainly on crustaceans which it gathers from the beds of rivers or ponds. It uses its powerful, ridged molars to crack the shells of its favourite prey.

Why does the crab-eating raccoon have such massive teeth?

The swamp rabbit found predominantly in Florida is a semi-aquatic rabbit. It lives in the marshes of the Gulf of Mexico. It makes its nest in swampy areas under cover of dense vegetation. Swamp rabbits are skilled swimmers but would be no match for a predator such as a dog. Their defence, if threatened, is to hide under an overhanging bush or floating vegetation, lying motionless in the water with only their nose exposed in order to breathe.

Which rabbit likes to swim?

The Delany's swamp mouse uses its long tail as a climbing aid in the dense shrub vegetation found in swamps and other wetlands. The range of this species is confined to a limited area in Central Africa. The Delany's swamp mouse was first discovered as recently as 1961.

Where does the Delany's swamp mouse make its home?

The North American meadow vole resembles the European field vole both in appearance and habit. It is the most widespread species of vole in North America. It is found in all moist habitats, where it builds a globular nest in tall grass.

What is the North American equivalent of the field vole?

This relative of the mole has a star-shaped circle of 22 pink, fleshy tentacles at the end of its snout, which are used to identify food by touch. In winter, it also functions as a fat storage reserve. Star-nosed moles are expert swimmers and divers. They live in wet, marshy regions adjoining water and are found in eastern Canada.

How does the star-nosed mole get its name?

Swamp rabbits are members of the cottontail family, so-called because of their tail, which resembles a ball of cotton wool.

Which marsupial has adapted most effectively to an aquatic habitat?

The water opossum, or yapok, lives along river-banks in tropical regions of South America. Its hind feet are webbed and function as paddles in the water. The water opossum has frog-like, sensitive fingers, which it uses to search the riverbed for molluscs, crustaceans and water insects, paddling slowly through shallow water as it feels for its prey. When swimming, it can also close off its ears.

What is the smallest living mammal?

The Etruscan pygmy shrew is just five centimetres long including the tail. Newborn pygmy shrews weigh just a fifth of a gram! This species of shrew is frequently found alongside streams in areas of dense, moist vegetation in southern Europe, South Asia and North Africa. Its tiny size makes it extremely susceptible to cold. If cold or deprived of food, it falls into a torpor to save energy.

What is the function of the trunk-like snout of the Pyrenean desman?

The Pyrenean desman has a flat, broad, trunk-like snout, ending in nostrils, which can be closed off by means of a valve. The elongated snout contains a large number of sensory cells and hairs providing the desman with an extremely touch-sensitive organ. It uses its snout to forage and grab prey and to transfer its prey to its mouth.

The Pyrenean desman inhabits mountain streams and rivers, as well as lakes up to an altitude of 2,200 metres in the northern section of the Iberian peninsula.

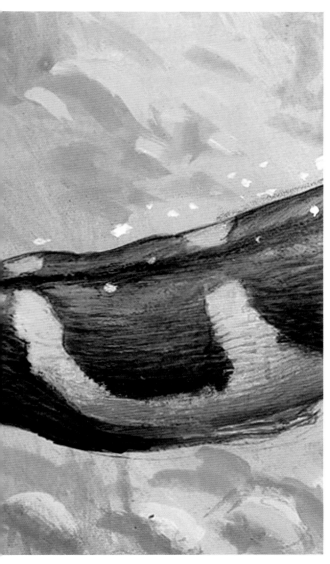

The water opossum cannot remain in water for too long as the water penetrates its fur. It is found from Mexico to Patagonia.

The Amazonian dolphin is around three metres long and weighs up to 160 kilograms, making it the largest species of river dolphin. They inhabit slow-moving waterways of the Amazon and Orinoco basins.

The river dolphin has an elongated crocodile-like snout and sharp, pointed teeth, which it uses to catch fish and to forage for crustaceans and other prey on the riverbed. The Ganges river dolphin has a very long, narrow snout, which is about one fifth of the dolphin's overall length.

Why does the river dolphin have such a long snout?

River dolphins, such as the Amazonian river dolphin, inhabit muddy, densely vegetated waters. Their tiny eyes are an adaptation to the fact that they can barely see their prey in such murky conditions. Instead, they find their way around by means of echolocation. They emit high-frequency sounds, which are bounced back off objects and plants. This sonar system is so accurate that dolphins are able to avoid copper a millimetre thick.

How do river dolphins find their way around?

The Amazonian manatee, measuring up to three metres in length, is the smallest species of manatee. It inhabits rivers and tributaries of the Amazon basin, where it feeds on aquatic plants, floating vegetation and palm fruits. Pollution, the damming of rivers and hunting have caused the population of Amazonian manatees to shrink to such an extent that they are now on the endangered list.

What is the smallest species of manatee?

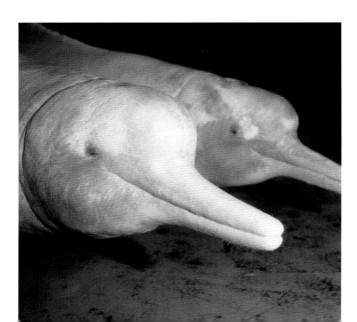

How does the mink locate its prey?

Before entering the water, the mink will first check whether there is any prey present. It does so by stretching its neck out over the water, keeping its head above water but with its sensory whiskers submerged. Tilting its head from side to side, it can monitor what is below the surface, plunging into the water once it has detected its prey.

How does the otter propel itself forwards in water?

Despite its somewhat awkward gait on land, in water the otter is an expert swimmer. For slow swimming it uses its legs as paddles, the webbing between its widely splayed toes providing additional propulsion. When swimming at speed, it folds its forelegs against its body and propels itself forwards by lateral movements of its tail.

How has the otter adapted to diving?

The otter has a thick fur and dense under fur that traps an insulating layer of air and prevents its body temperature from dropping too low. The fur is also kept oiled and water-repellent by secretions from special glands. The otter's nostrils and small, round ears have valves which can be closed when submerged. It can remain underwater for up to four minutes and reach speeds of up to 12 kilometres per hour when chasing prey.

Otters not only inhabit rivers and lakes but are also found in saltwater environments in Western Europe and Scandinavia. Their diet consists of fish, small mammals, waterfowl, amphibians and invertebrates.

The mink is an expert swimmer and diver. Once it has detected its prey in water, it seizes it with its mouth and hides it on land.

The massive water buffalo can grow up to three metres in length and stand two metres high at shoulder height. Its horns can measure two metres across.

Where does the giant otter make its home?

The giant otter's habitat is among the slow-moving rivers and streams of the South American rainforest. It constructs resting places on the banks of rivers.

How does the marsh mongoose differ from other species of mongoose?

The marsh mongoose is crepuscular in habit and its paws, in contrast to other species, are not webbed. This enables it to splay its toes widely and move with ease on boggy ground. The marsh mongoose inhabits dense vegetation on the banks of rivers and lakes and is also found in swamps and mangroves.

No, it is a type of mongoose resembling an otter in appearance. Like the otter, it has broad, webbed feet and its nostrils and ears are equipped with valves that can be closed in water. The otter civet lies in wait for its prey, which includes fish, small mammals and birds, in the manner of a crocodile.

The dark-grey coloured water buffalo is a social animal that lives in a family group or in large herds. It spends the day wallowing in muddy pools or water. If a mud bath is not deep enough, the buffalo will use its horns to toss mud onto its back. In this way, it tries to rid itself of irritating insects. If this fails to work, it submerges itself in water so that only its head or even just its nose is visible. Water buffalo feed in the evening or at night on aquatic plants or grasses and herbs.

Is the otter civet a relative of the otter?

How does a water buffalo spend its day?

EXTREME HABITATS

There is no region on earth that has not been occupied by mammals. Even regions with extreme climates have become home to various species of mammal. Any creature intending to make its permanent home in such extreme conditions will, however, have to adapt in a very specialised way. To some extent, islands, even ones as big as Australia, which is a continent in its own right, are also extreme environments where various forms of life, which do not exist elsewhere, have been left to evolve in isolation from the rest of the world. Such species become endangered when they are suddenly confronted with unfamiliar animals.

How do chamois keep their footing even on steep slopes?

Chamois have cloven hooves that can be splayed wide apart and an elastic base with a strongly developed, hard, sharp edge. They also have a soft pad which provides them with good traction in their usual terrain.

Why do chamois rub their horns?

Only the bucks engage in this activity, but not to rub the velvet off, as deer do – instead they rub their horns against branches, to deposit a musk-scented secretion produced by a scent gland at the base of the horns. This serves to mark their territory.

Which mammal is the North American equivalent of the chamois?

The mountain goat, native to the Rocky Mountains, is easily distinguished by its white shaggy coat. Like chamois, these mammals are extremely sure-footed climbers. The Rocky Mountain goat feeds on grasses and herbs found in high-altitude pastures.

How do alpine ibex males determine rank?

Male ibexes live throughout the year in bachelor groups, governed by a strict hierarchy. Only the dominant buck will mate with the females. The question of rank is settled in the summer when rival males rear on their hind legs, lunge forward and swing their heads at their adversary. Their heavy horns clash loudly as they collide.

The 'gamsbart', literally 'chamois beard', is a tuft of hair traditionally used to decorate local costumes in alpine regions and is made from the long, stiff hairs taken from the animal's withers. In fights with rival males, the bucks can erect these hairs to make themselves look bigger.

The impressive, curved horns of an adult alpine ibex can weigh up to four kilograms and grow up to one metre in length.

Alpine ibex have been known to reach the age of fourteen years in the wild. Their age can be determined from their horns. The horns stop growing during the mating season and growth restarts once it is over. This results in the formation of a dark lateral line around the horn. The number of rings indicates the animal's age in years.

What age can alpine ibex reach?

In fights between rival males, the snow sheep of Siberia will run towards each other at full tilt and crash horns together. The sheep's brain is protected by a double layer of protective bone that cushions these mighty blows. To protect the animal's neck, the skull is linked to the neck vertebrae by a special hinged joint.

How do snow sheep withstand such severe blows to the head?

In contrast to the rather stocky and compact snow or dall sheep, which are expert climbers, the long legs of the argalis make them good runners. These animals live at elevations of 6,000 metres in the mountains of Russia, China and Mongolia.

Why is the argali or mountain sheep regarded as a fast runner?

The takin is found in the mountains of Central China at altitudes of 2,000 to 5,000 metres, where it inhabits rhododendron forests, bamboo thickets or small stands of shrubs. The takin is one of the rarest and most endangered animals in the world. Scientific opinion cannot agree as to its classification vis-à-vis other mammals (taxonomy).

Where does the takin live?

The chiru, or Tibetan antelope, has air sacs in its nostrils which it can dilate to the size of pigeons' eggs. Male chirus do this especially during the mating season. These air sacs are believed to amplify the bucks' vocal calls. Chirus live in Tibet above the tree line at altitudes of 4,500 metres.

Why does the chiru's muzzle appear swollen?

Which cat inhabits high mountainous regions?

The snow leopard is native to the mountains of Central Asia and can be found at altitudes of up to 6,000 metres. Its beautiful, thick fur offers excellent protection from the cold.

Which camel is the smallest in the world?

The vicuña stands about one metre high at the shoulder and weighs no more than 55 kilograms. Its graceful appearance is enhanced by its long neck, its long legs and rounded head. Vicuñas are found at altitudes of up to 5,500 metres on the Altiplano, the area of high plateau in the Andes.

What are the distinguishing characteristics of the white-lipped deer?

This is the most specialised species of Old World mountain deer and it lives in the mountains of Tibet and other mountainous regions of Asia at altitudes of up to 5,000 metres. This expert climber can traverse steep mountain slopes at high speed thanks to its large hooves, which are rounded at the front and equipped with long, well-developed dewclaws so the animal can move with surefootedness. The hairs on its back run in the opposite direction to the rest of its fur. The hairs run from front to back as far as its belly and then the lie is reversed on its rump. This may be an adaptation to changing wind directions or whirlwinds.

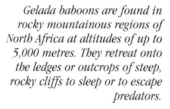

Gelada baboons are found in rocky mountainous regions of North Africa at altitudes of up to 5,000 metres. They retreat onto the ledges or outcrops of steep, rocky cliffs to sleep or to escape predators.

Of all the New World deer species, the Andean deer is best suited for life in high mountainous regions. There is a northern and a southern type of Andean deer: the North Andean deer prefers higher altitudes. Its outer coat is coarse and thick with soft underfur. Each individual hair has a hollow shaft, which holds trapped air. This provides the animal with good heat insulation as well as making its coat water-repellent.

What is the New World equivalent of the white-lipped deer?

Both males and females of this species of baboon have an hourglass-shaped red patch of skin located on the throat and chest. In males, this patch of colour is surrounded by white hair, whilst in the females the area is surrounded by numerous white blisters, which swell up when the female is ready to mate. The bare skin also turns bright red. The female's genital area is also similarly coloured.

Why is the gelada baboon nicknamed the 'bleeding heart baboon'?

The mountains of North America and the steppes and mountains of Central Asia are home to a species of mammal, known as a pika or rock rabbit, which calls or 'sings' either individually, in chorus or in duet. This has led to the nickname 'whistling hare'. They do not hibernate over winter.

Is there such a thing as a whistling hare?

As an adaptation to the high altitudes at which they live, vicuñas have large hearts – about 50 per cent bigger than those in mammals of a similar size.

North American pikas store large hoards of dried grass in established sites under stones. They will feed on these stores of food during the winter.

How do marmots prepare for hibernation?

Marmots hibernate for about eight months of the year. In preparation, they lay down a reserve of fat during the summer by eating herbs, grasses and fresh shoots, virtually doubling their weight in the process. In the autumn, they line the sleeping chambers in their burrows with dried grass. Before hibernating, they block up the entrances to the burrow with earth and plant material.

How do marmots communicate with one another?

Marmots live in family groups and are socially extremely interactive. They greet by touching noses and engage in mutual grooming. Marmots mark their territory by smearing a secretion from their cheek glands along its borders. Sentries warn other members of the group of the presence of a predator by emitting a series of warning whistles. The appearance of an airborne predator is signalled by high-pitched alarm whistles.

Where do puna mice make their home?

This small species of rodent lives at an altitude of between 4,400 to 5,200 metres in the Altiplano of South America. Active by day, they protect themselves from the cold at night by hiding in their warm burrows built in crevices under rocks. Puna mice were first discovered in 1939 and resemble the snow vole.

Mountain viscachas are social creatures, which live in colonies on the inaccessible slopes of the Peruvian Andes at altitudes ranging from 900 to 5,000 metres.

Due to its silky fur, the wild chinchilla has now become an endangered species.

Alpine marmots originally only occurred in the Central and Western Alps and the Carpathian Mountains. They were later released in the Pyrenees, the Eastern Alps and the Black Forest region of Germany.

The mountain vole is found in the rocky mountainous regions of Central Asia where it occupies an ecological niche equivalent to that of the snow vole. Mountain voles stockpile herbs and grass in established, protected sites, frequently turning the plant material over until it is dry. The dried grass is then stored in the crevices of rocky cliffs.

How do Asian voles store their food?

Although the snow vole is found in the Alps at altitudes almost as high as the snow line, it actually occupies areas where there is very little snow. It requires rocky surroundings where it can hide in crevices among the rocks. Where digging is possible, snow voles will hollow out short burrows.

Does the snow vole live in a snowy environment?

This species of guinea pig lives in colonies in the grassy plains and scrublands of South America from Colombia to Argentina. It is also found in the Andes up to an altitude of 5,000 metres. The colony is divided into various smaller groups. When foraging for food, they follow specific trails running through their territories.

Where do Brazilian guinea pigs live?

In order to detect the presence of a predator at night or to find food, an animal must possess exceptionally good sensory organs. The chinchilla has distinctively big eyes and ears. Movable whiskers around its nose help the chinchilla find its way around in the dark.

What features of the chinchilla suggest that it is a nocturnal animal?

Mountain viscachas are members of the guinea pig family. They spend their nights in caves and rocky crevices on the steep slopes of the Andes at altitudes of up to 5,000 metres. These social creatures live in family groups, several of which combine to form a colony. When feeding, one viscacha will keep watch and warn its companions if it detects a predator, whereupon the whole colony will quickly vanish into their burrows.

What are mountain viscachas?

How has the polar bear adapted to life in the cold?

The polar bear's thick fur provides excellent insulation. Its hairs are hollow and translucent. They absorb UV light and act as fiberoptic tubes to conduct light to the animal's black skin. Ninety-five per cent of the sun's UV rays can be converted into heat in this way. It also has a thick layer of fat beneath its skin and on the soles of its feet, which are protected by a covering of fur.

How do polar bears catch their prey?

Polar bears are expert swimmers and excellent divers. They can bring their prey up to the water's surface from depths of over four metres. Diving under water, they pounce on sea birds from below and swim in pursuit of seals and dolphins. When hunting for seals, polar bears crouch near the seal's breathing hole in the ice and wait for it to appear. They can also leap suddenly out of the water and seize a seal on the edge of the ice.

Do polar bears have a good sense of smell?

Polar bears can smell their prey from 30 kilometres away. Individual bears have been known to detect prey from 60 kilometres away. They can detect and seize seals from underneath the ice and snow.

Why do land mammals exist in the Arctic but not in the Antartic?

The Antarctic is surrounded by water and effectively isolated. When conditions become intolerable, land mammals would be unable to escape and would inevitably die. The Arctic, on the other hand, is linked by land bridges to the mainland in the south so that land mammals can move south across the ice in winter and eventually return to the Arctic by the same route.

How do animals survive conditions in the snow and ice?

The mountain hare, the Arctic fox and the stoat all grow a white coat in winter, providing them with excellent camouflage. The hare's winter fur is thicker for greater protection against the cold and has the additional effect of broadening its paws to stop it sinking into the snow. Fur on the underside of the paw helps keep its feet warm.

Polar bears roam about a great deal. Walking at a steady pace, they can cover about four kilometres an hour. If they are being pursued, they can reach speeds of up to 40 kilometres per hour. In water, they are able to swim at the rate of ten kilometres per hour.

The walrus is immediately recognisable thanks to its long tusks protruding from a relatively small head and its whiskery 'moustache', which it uses to feel around for food on the ground.

Comparing northern species of animals with related southern species, it is clear that the northern varieties are larger than the southern ones. A larger body produces a good deal of heat and heat loss is reduced due to the surface area being comparatively small in relation to the animal's bulk. In other words, it stores heat better than a small body. The extremities of such animals, such as the ears and tail, are also much smaller, further reducing the overall surface area.

The walrus uses its tusks, which are the extended canines of its upper jaw, to prise molluscs from the seabed or to lever itself onto an ice floe. Occasionally, the tusks are used as ice picks to help the walrus climb over ice and rocks. They are also a useful defence weapon in combat against rival males during the mating season.

What does the walrus use its tusks for?

At birth, the walrus measures just one metre in length and weighs 50 kilograms. Thanks to its mother's rich milk, the baby walrus grows very quickly but it is not weaned for two years. It follows its mother straight into the water. When it becomes tired, the mother will carry it on her back, protecting it between her front flippers in the event of danger.

How does a young walrus develop?

Northern fur seals can withstand sea temperatures of between 8 and 12 °C thanks to a layer of dense fur beneath the bristly guard hairs. It is estimated that there are 50,000 individual hairs to each square centimetre, rendering the fur waterproof.

How does the northern fur seal get its name?

These islands provide the breeding grounds for most of the 1.7 million fur seals. The bulls are first to arrive and lay claim to a breeding site along the coast. The females follow somewhat later and go ashore in the territory of the bull of their choice, give birth to their calf and mate thereafter. Each female can identify her offspring by its call and smell.

Why do northern fur seals visit the Pribilof Islands?

The male of this species has a nose, which in its flaccid state resembles a short trunk. When inflated, it becomes a large black bulge sitting on its head like a balloon-shaped cap. Hooded seal males can also inflate their nasal cavity out through their nostrils so that it resembles a red balloon.

How does the hooded seal get its name?

Fur seals in pursuit of their favourite prey, such as fish or squid, can reach speeds of up to 30 kilometres per hour.

Why is it sometimes a fatal mistake for a harp seal to come up to breathe at an ice hole?

Like all marine mammals, harp seals have to come to the surface to breathe. When the sea is iced over in winter, seals create and maintain an ice-free breathing hole, where they can come up for air. Occasionally, a polar bear will patiently lie in wait by such an ice hole until a seal surfaces and then kill it with a single blow of its mighty paw.

Where does the Arctic ringed seal make its home?

The ringed seal lives in the waters of the Arctic and the Subarctic. Its young are born into a world covered with snow, where their white baby coats (lanugo) provide them with perfect camouflage. Ringed seals spend most of their time below the ice, but they have to keep a breathing hole open in the ice where they can get ashore. Once snow has covered over a breathing hole, a female seal will hollow out a cave around the hole, creating a lair where it can rest and give birth to its young.

What do crabeater seals feed on?

This species of seal, which is native to the Antarctic, does not, as its name suggests, prey on crabs but on tiny crustaceans called krill. The seals can strain krill from the water thanks to their specially adapted teeth. The upper and lower molars have bony protuberances on them, creating a filtering system when they are pressed together.

Like many other species of seal, the male Weddell seal will stake out its territory in preparation for mating. These underwater territories surround breathing holes and landing areas used by the females.

Baby harp seals have white fur, which they retain for a short time after birth. Every year hundreds of thousands of baby seals are clubbed to death – killed for their white coats.

The Weddell seal gives birth to her young on the Antarctic continent. When the seals surface from depths of anything up to 700 metres, their biggest problem is to find a breathing hole in the ice. Their ability to remain underwater for over 80 minutes without breathing allows them plenty of time for searching.

Which is the world's southern-most seal species?

This is the name given to the thick layer of fat beneath the skin of walruses, seals, sea cows and whales. The fat provides insulation against the cold and produces a degree of elasticity in the skin that reduces turbulence. The males of some species of seal draw on this layer of fat during the breeding season when all they have time for is fighting over territory and defending their females. Millions of seals have been killed for their blubber, which can be rendered down into oil.

What is blubber?

The bowhead or Greenland right whale belongs to the class of right whales. Right whales are, commercially speaking, the most valuable whales. Greenland whales have the thickest layer of blubber (50 centimetres) and the longest whalebone, and for this reason they are the most popular targets for harpooning.

Why is the bowhead whale classed as a right whale?

The barrel-shaped Greenland right whale measures up to 20 metres in length and weighs up to 80 tonnes. The whalebone or baleen, measuring over four metres, is the longest of any whale.

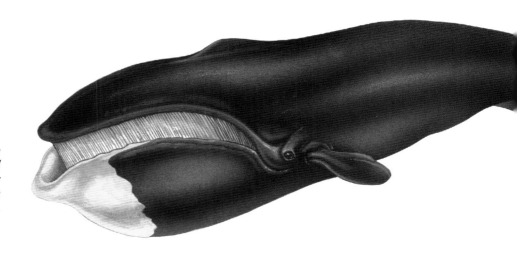

How do musk ox defend their young?

If threatened, adult musk oxen will form a ring around the calf with their heads facing outward. The predator, possibly a wolf pack, then finds itself face to face with the musk oxen's huge heads and mighty horns. If the wolves attack, the musk oxen will lower their heads and ram their opponent.

What is the mammal with the longest coat?

The hairs on the musk ox's neck and flanks can be up to 90 centimetres long. Their thick coat provides the animals with good protection against the cold.

Why do reindeer or caribou migrate?

Reindeer or caribou spend the summer months in the Arctic tundra where they feed on nutrient-rich plants. When food supplies dwindle in the autumn, they migrate 500 to 1,000 kilometres to the forest tundra, where they feed on buds, lichen, especially reindeer moss, and other plants, which are concealed beneath the snow. They scrape away the snow with their hooves so they can feed and, in spring, they return to the north.

When are reindeer calves born?

Reindeer calves are born in spring. They are so well developed at birth that by the very next day, they are able to move with the rest of the herd.

The horns of a musk ox merge together on its forehead, forming a kind of helmet. The single horn of a musk ox bull can grow up to 60 centimetres in length.

Reindeer are the only species of deer in which the females carry antlers as well as the males. The antlers are shed each year and regrown afresh.

Snow hares are found over a wide range of regions from the tundra and forest tundra of Eurasia to North America and Greenland. In addition, populations of subspecies also exist in the Alps and in Japan.

Why are Dall sheep sometimes known as thinhorn sheep?

The horns of Dall sheep are usually thinner at the base, though somewhat longer, than those of thick horn sheep and the tips are less likely to break off during combat.

How has the reindeer adapted to boggy ground?

Reindeer have broad hooves with rounded edges. The 'toes' are connected by a membrane, enabling the animals to splay their hooves widely to gain a better foothold. This broad surface area helps prevent them sinking into the ground. The reindeer's dewclaws are also situated very close to the ground for extra grip.

This species of hare lives in the forest tundra and taiga of North America. To prevent it sinking in the snow, the soles of the snowshoe hare's feet are covered with dense fur, forming the 'snowshoe'. Humans wear snowshoes for exactly the same purpose.

The snow or mountain hare's coat consists of a white undercoat and a layer of guard hairs. It is the latter which moult and determine the colour of the hare's fur. The change of colour from brown to white is triggered by the ambient temperature. Mountain hares which live in the tundra remain white all year round whilst populations inhabiting more southerly regions together with the alpine species turn white from about mid-October and develop a brown coat again from mid-February onward. In Scotland and the Faroe islands, mountain hares stay brown all year. All mountain hares have black-tipped ears.

How does the snowshoe hare get its name?

When does the snow hare change into its white coat?

Why do young wolf cubs play?

Wolf cubs play to practice all the behaviour skills they need to survive. These skills include slinking, pouncing on prey, sprinting in spurts, developing fast reactions and working as part of a team with the rest of the pack. By building up their reserves of courage and endurance, young wolves can achieve higher status within the pack hierarchy.

What is the purpose of pack hierarchy among wolves?

Pack hierarchy ensures peaceful co-existence among the pack members. The question of rank is settled by ritualised contests, which seldom end in serious injury. The pack leader, or alpha male, can be identified by his high tail position and the fact that he is first to feed on any captured prey.

What does the Arctic fox feed on?

It preys on small mammals, especially lemmings, birds and their eggs, fish, invertebrates and carrion, but will also eat berries. When cliff-nesting birds are rearing their young, Arctic foxes enjoy an abundance of food. When normal prey is in scarce supply, Arctic foxes will share the leftovers of prey captured by polar bears, wolves or wolverines, waiting patiently until these larger predators are finished. They also eat the cadavers of whales and seals, which they find along the coast.

During the summer, the Arctic fox has a greyish-brown coat that turns white in winter.

Wolves are found in a wide variety of habitats, including the tundra and the taiga of Eurasia and North America, the steppes, as well as semi-arid and mountainous regions.

Arctic foxes abandon their roaming lifestyle during the breeding season and occupy a den with their mate. Dens can be complex systems of burrows which have previously been home to generations of foxes. They can be identifed from the air by differences in vegetation around the den compared with the surrounding area. This results from digging and territorial scent marking with urine.

What does an Arctic fox's den look like?

The Canadian lynx is smaller than the European lynx and has a shorter tail. Its longer hind legs make it taller at the back. Both species have thick pads of hair on the soles of their paws in winter, although those of the Canadian species are denser.

How does the Canadian lynx differ from the European lynx?

No. The unsociable mountain lemming is subject to population fluctuations every three to four years. A rise in population density leads to food becoming scarce, causing the lemmings to migrate in large numbers in search of fresh sources of food. If they reach a dead end, such as a cliff top above an ocean, the lemmings stop and a large throng will build up until those in front are pushed into the water as more and more lemmings arrive. If conditions are calm, lemmings can swim well but will drown if the water is rough.

Do mountain lemmings really commit suicide?

As they search for food during the winter, mountain lemmings construct a complex system of tunnels under the snow where these unsociable creatures make their solitary home. To cope with this digging activity, the claws on their front paws grow longer in winter than in summer.

What are lemurs?

Lemurs are members of a group of primates known as prosimians, which are native only to Madagascar and the Comoros islands. Thanks to its insular existence the lemur has evolved into a number of adapted species, which resemble apes in Africa or Asia. For example, sifaka lemurs are similar to gibbons whilst maki lemurs resemble bush babies. Lemurs inhabit all types of habitat. They rely heavily on their excellent sense of smell.

Why does the aye-aye have such long fingers?

Aye-ayes have unusually long fingers – the middle finger is particularly elongated and thin. It finds food by tapping on trees with its fingers. From the sounds produced, aye-ayes identify the location of grubs, and gnaw holes in the wood using their teeth and claws, before poking their long middle finger into the hole to reach the larvae.

Why do ring-tailed lemurs have such a distinctive tail?

On the ground, ring-tailed lemurs carry their tail stiffly upright in the air as a signal to others in the group. The males also use their tails to display. They smear their tail with a secretion from a gland on their upper arm, then wave it around their head like a lasso to spread the scent as far as possible.

After a cool night, colourful sifaka lemurs warm themselves up each morning by sunbathing.

Despite its plump appearance, the lesser hedgehog tenrec is good at climbing trees in search of food.

The aye-aye lives in rain-forests, mangroves or bamboo thickets. It forages for food at night and spends the daylight hours sleeping in a carefully constructed tree nest, measuring about 50 centimetres in diameter.

Indri lemurs were considered sacred because the natives of Madagascar believed that they were the reincarnated form of their dead ancestors. Indris are the largest species of prosimian ape.

The mouse lemur is just 11 to 13 centimetres tall and its bushy, hairy tail is the same length as its body. This tiny nocturnal creature falls into a kind of torpor when temperatures drop or in periods of drought. During this time, it relies on stores of fat in its rear legs and at the base of its tail. The mouse lemur feeds on fruit, flowers, nectar, insects, small reptiles and birds.

On the ground, these animals run and hop (up to four metres at a time) from an upright position standing on their back legs with their arms held high. They also leap from tree to tree. Their bodies are horizontal as they jump, but they straighten up into a vertical position just before landing on a branch with their arms and legs outstretched. In this way, they are capable of covering a distance of ten metres in a single jump.

The fossa is a type of Madagascan mongoose. In appearance, it bears a marked resemblance to a mountain lion. The fossa has two fearsome cat-like teeth in its upper and lower jaw with which it tears up its prey.

This is the lesser hedgehog tenrec although, despite their appearance, these primitive insectivores are not related to hedgehogs at all. They do have various characteristics in common, including their spine-covered back, the ability to roll themselves into a ball and their habit of spitting on themselves during the mating season.

Which mammal resembles a cross between a duck, an otter and a beaver?

The platypus has a large, flat bill with nostrils on top, its toes are webbed and it lays eggs. Once hatched, however, the young, like all mammals, are fed by their mother's milk. The milk is released through the skin in various places on the mother's abdomen. The body of the platypus is completely covered with fur.

What does the koala feed on?

The koala specialises in a diet of leaves and bark from around 20 species of eucalyptus. Other varieties contain too many toxic compounds.

What function is served by the koala's long intestine?

Relative to its body size, the koala has the longest intestine of all mammals (2.5 metres). It is home to large numbers of micro-organisms which help the koala digest its food. A young koala ingests these micro-organisms when it switches from mother's milk to a diet of leaves. To this end the mother excretes a special kind of intestinal soup.

How does the honey possum feed?

The little honey possum is barely ten centimetres tall and relies on the large blossoms of banksia and dryandra for its supply of nectar and pollen. To blot up the nectar, the tip of the honey possum's tongue is like a brush and on the roof of its mouth, this tiny mammal has a ridge of horn with which it can scrape the pollen and nectar off its tongue.

What does the woylie use to line its nest?

This miniature version of a kangaroo spends the day sleeping in its well-lined nest situated beneath shrubs or in hollowed out depressions. Since its tiny front legs can scarcely carry anything, it has developed a special system for transporting nesting material. It piles up dry grass and leaves, using its mouth and front paws, then grabs hold of the bundle with its tail and carries it off to the nest.

The platypus inhabits lakes and slow-moving rivers in southern Australia and Tasmania. The male has a venomous spur on its hind feet; the venom is capable of killing a dog.

Every child is familiar with the koala, a marsupial – their cute appearance makes them popular as teddy bears.

Marsupials are a primitive group of mammals which give birth early to very immature young. The babies continue developing in their mother's pouch, firmly attached to a nipple. Most Australian mammals, for example, kangaroos and koalas, are marsupials, as well as many South American species, such as the water opossum. Even more primitive are egg-laying mammals, which lay and incubate their eggs, then suckle their young after they hatch.

The coat of the male giant red kangaroo gets its colour from a kind of powder secreted by glands on its throat and chest, which it sprinkles evenly over its body.

They live in arid and semi-arid regions in open, scrubland or grassy plains with isolated trees. They are well adapted to their desert habitat and pant to keep themselves cool. They also lick their chest, arms and legs – as the saliva evaporates, it helps cool them down. The crouching position they adopt minimises the heat they absorb from their surroundings.

Where do giant red kangaroos live?

Like the hyena, the Tasmanian devil feeds primarily on the remains of prey left by other animals or on other carrion. It performs a useful function in terms of public health since decomposing cadavers can harbour all kinds of disease.

Which Tasmanian mammal performs a similar function to the hyena?

Its first defence against danger is to flee into its burrow and block the entrance with its hindquarters. The wombat's thick fur and tough hide make it difficult for a predator to harm or dislodge it. If it is followed it into its burrow, the wombat may crush its adversary against the roof of the burrow.

How does the common wombat defend itself against enemies?

This species of mouse, one of the few true mice in Australia, feeds on grasses and seeds. In cultivated areas, it has developed a fondness for sugar cane, which is also a species of grass. It climbs the tall canes and gnaws on them from the outside. The problem is not that it gnaws the sugar cane but that the damage caused makes the cane prone to disease and collapse.

Why is the grasslands melomys unpopular in Australia?

Dingos are persistent hunters, pursuing their prey over long distances. Once they catch up with a kangaroo, they will encircle it. The dominant male leads the attack but must be wary of the kangaroo's sharp claws. The rest of the pack then joins the fray. A solitary dingo is not strong enough to overpower a giant kangaroo alone – a successful attack relies upon mobbing the victim.

How do dingos overpower a giant kangaroo?

Which seal is native to the Galapagos islands?

The Galapagos sea lion is smaller than its relative, the Californian sea lion. It is found all over the archipelago wherever there are sandy beaches. The highpoint for visitors to the islands is seeing the sea lions frolicking inquisitively amongst swimmers and snorkelers.

Which is the smallest fur seal?

The Galapagos fur seal grows to up to1.6 metres in length and weighs approximately 70 kilograms. Although really a type of sea lion, this seal gets its name from its dense fur. Its thick coat is also the reason why it lives along the archipelago's rocky cliffs where it can avoid the intense sunshine by sheltering in the shade of rocks and caves.

Were any species of mammal endemic to the Galapagos?

The only mammals on the Galapagos islands which were not introduced by man are rice rats, which are thought to have arrived from Central America on floating vegetation.

What is the Indian grey mongoose doing on the Comoros?

This species of mongoose was released in the Comoro Islands by man as a means of controlling the rat population. Unfortunately, they are now decimating the native species, which are not equipped to defend themselves against foreign predators.

The Indian grey mongoose stands on its hind feet to survey its surroundings. It can be distinguished from its relative, the small Indian mongoose, by the gold shimmer on its fur.

Hutias are native to the islands of the West Indies. Of the 30 species originally recorded, many have become extinct or are endangered. They have perished as a result of the introduction of predators such as the mongoose or domestic pets, like dogs. Man, too, has contributed to their disappearance by destroying their habitat.

Which rodent is native to the islands of the West Indies?

Endemic means that a particular species of animal lives only within a restricted area, for example on an island.

What is meant by 'endemic'?

Crete is home to an endemic species of spiny mouse with stiff, spiny hairs on its back. It lives in arid, stony areas in the mountains or amongst low-growing steppe vegetation. If its food has a high moisture content, it does not need to drink.

Which rodent is endemic to Crete?

The Sumatran rabbit is the only member of the rabbit family to have striped fur. It lives on the forested slopes of the Barisan Mountains in western Sumatra at an altitude of between 600 and 1,400 metres. These nocturnal creatures spend the day sleeping in caves or burrows. They feed on the young shoots and leaves of various forest plants but do not eat bark.

What rabbit has a striped coat?

During the mating season, the male Galapagos sea lion bulls gather a harem of females and defend their coastal territories against rival males.

Other than the Galapagos sea lions, the Galapagos fur seals are the only seals to inhabit this archipelago. The males of this species are far larger than the females.

SETTLEMENTS

Since the beginning of time, conditions on earth have been constantly changing. Volcanic eruptions, climate fluctuations and meteorite strikes have all caused massive changes. What is more, living creatures themselves are also instrumental in transforming their natural surroundings. Human beings, however, have wrought the most significant changes and have created settlements, which are nowadays constructed largely from man-made materials. Yet even these habitats have been colonised by various species of animals possessing a particular talent for adaptation. Some species of animals and plants have even been modified by man to suit his needs.

How does the hedgehog make its spines stick up?

The hedgehog's back is completely covered with an armour-like layer of muscle. If the hedgehog is startled or threatened, this muscle contracts, turning the hedgehog into a ball with its head, legs and tail tucked inside. As the skin on its back becomes taut, the spines stand erect.

Why do we sometimes see dead hedgehogs on roads?

Hedgehogs instinctively curl up into a ball when faced with danger. This provides excellent protection when confronted by a fox but is not an effective defence against an approaching car.

Which shrew plays a useful role in the house and garden?

The greater white-toothed shrew makes its home all-year round in houses, cellars and barns where it feeds on spiders, wood lice, beetles and even mice. Outdoors it preys on garden pests, such as wireworms, grubs and snails.

What is our most common species of bat?

The pipistrelle bat is the smallest European bat species and is found during the summer months in gardens and parks, often preying on insects attracted to the light of street lamps. Pipistrelles spend the daylight hours sleeping in cracks and crevices of trees, behind window shutters, or in the walls of houses.

A fully-grown hedgehog has around 16,000 spines, each about two to three centimetres long. Newborn hedgehogs have spines measuring just two to three millimetres in length. They are white and still very soft at birth.

House mice are both fast runners and good climbers. They can balance on swaying wires, run up and down smooth cables and climb up vertical walls. Members of a family group have an individual smell, by which they recognise each other. White mice of this species are generally used for laboratory experiments.

Which mammals occupy bird nesting boxes?

In the event of a shortage of hollow trees, dormice will take over and give birth in bird nesting boxes from June/July onwards. They spend the day asleep and emerge at night to forage for berries, fruits and seeds. A nesting box which is home to a dormouse family can be identified by the droppings on the roof.

How does the brown rat differ from the black rat?

The brown rat is distinctly larger and more powerful than the black rat and has a shorter tail. It also has a blunter snout and smaller ears. The brown rat's incisors are orange-red in colour at the front.

Where does the brown rat make its home in urban developments?

Brown rats colonise sewers, cellars and rubbish tips in any populated area. They represent the most common wild mammal found living in urban settlements. It is estimated that for every human resident, there is at least one rat living in a town's sewage system.

Are 'house mice' the only mice found in houses?

No, wood mice and yellow-necked mice also take up residence inside houses at the onset of autumn and winter, and sometimes make their home in attics. From here, they can supplement their normal diet of plant material with insects, worms or dead animals. In this respect, they have a less specialised diet than field mice, for example.

Which mouse has the most widespread distribution?

The house mouse is thought to have originated from the steppes and semi-arid regions of Africa and Asia. It has lived close to humans since prehistoric times and has been spread by humans to all parts of the globe. It has ranged as far as it has thanks to the fact that it will eat just about anything and can find shelter anywhere. It reproduces just as successfully in underground tube stations as in refrigeration plants or warehouses storing curd soap (which it is known to eat!).

Are the rabbits we see in urban parks truly wild?

All the rabbits living in Central and Western Europe are the descendants of rabbits that escaped in the Middle Ages from compounds known as rabbit gardens. In those days, young rabbits were regarded as fasting meat. Many of the rabbits we see in parks are in fact domestic pets, which have been released. They adapt quickly to life in the wild as their behaviour still corresponds largely to that of their wild ancestors.

Who or what is known as the 'car marten'?

This is not in fact a car thief but a mammal called the stone marten, which has developed the habit of biting through rubber car parts. It specialises in ignition wires, brake cables and rubber seals. The reason for this behaviour remains a mystery.

What is the stone marten's favourite prey?

This mammal feeds mainly on other creatures killed on the road, thereby fulfilling an important role in public health. It will also rummage through rubbish bins in the hope of finding edible leftovers. Fungi, fruits and berries likewise form part of its diet. Stone martens are extremely versatile which is undoubtedly one of the reasons for their success. Young birds and eggs, as well as other small vertebrates are also welcome additions to their menu.

Wild rabbits were originally native to the Iberian Peninsula. They were farmed for their tender meat by the Romans, who introduced them to many different parts of the globe.

Their slender bodies enable stone martens to slip through cracks in walls and holes in roofs in order to build nests in attics. Their antics can sometimes make people think there is a ghost in the house.

In its Hindu homeland, the Hanuman langur or common langur is revered as the living embodiment of the god Hanuman.

What do town-dwelling badgers and foxes live on?

They raid litter bins and dustbins, scavenging for bits of leftover food or sandwiches found in school playgrounds. They also rummage through compost heaps.

Which mammal is also known as the Toddy Cat?

It is the Asian palm civet, a cat-sized mammal native to Southeast Asia. Toddy is the juice derived from palm trees and fermented into wine. The palm civet is very fond of this juice and has changed his preferred habitat from the forest to urban areas. His favourite food comprises pineapple, bananas and mangoes, as well as small mammals and insects.

Hanuman langurs are regarded as sacred in many parts of India and revered as descendants of the god Hanuman, the guardian of villages. Since they cannot be hunted or killed and are fed by the devout Indians, they are not on the endangered species list.

Several sub-species of this mammal are found all over the Indian subcontinent, from Nepal to the southern tip of India and as far as Sri Lanka. They have populated every kind of habitat, from snow-covered mountain regions up to altitudes of 4,000 metres, to semi-arid regions and rainforests as well as towns and villages.

Many wild animals, such as foxes, badgers and opossums, have, thanks to their remarkable capacity for adaptation and the fact that they are omnivorous, succeeded in populating urban areas.

Why do we often see Hanuman langurs within temple grounds?

Where do Hanuman langurs live?

Why do wild animals live in towns?

How long have domestic horses existed?

As long as 5,000 to 6,000 years ago, nomads from the steppes of Eurasia began domesticating the wild horse. They used it for riding and carrying their belongings.

What is the world's smallest horse called?

It is the falabella miniature horse which was developed in Argentina near Buenos Aires. Bred by crossing very small Shetland ponies with very small thoroughbred stallions, Falabella horses stand just 76 centimetres tall at shoulder height.

What is a draught horse?

A draught or dray horse is one of the European species of horse bred for hard, heavy tasks. They have broad, compact bodies and relatively short, solid legs. Draught horses can develop great strength and are used to pull heavy machinery and vehicles.

What is the difference between a mule and a hinny?

Both are the offspring of horses and donkeys. Mules are the offspring of a male donkey and female horse, whereas hinnies are the result of a cross between a male horse and a female donkey. Both the mule and the hinny are usually infertile.

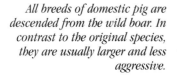

All breeds of domestic pig are descended from the wild boar. In contrast to the original species, they are usually larger and less aggressive.

A stallion curls its lips up to bare its teeth. This is known as the 'Flehmen' response. It draws in air through a passage connecting the mouth cavity with the Jacobson's organ above the hard palate. This enables the stallion to check whether a female is producing sex-stimulating chemicals (pheromones) in her urine. Nerve cells in the Jacobson organ relay messages to the olfactory centre of the brain and the part that governs sexual behaviour. If the stallion picks up the scent of pheromones, it will make advances to the mare.

What does it mean when horses curl their lips?

These are the only species of deer to be domesticated and the only species in which both males and females have antlers. Unlike other species, the antlers are not symmetrical. The Sami people (formerly referred to as the Lapps) keep herds of semi-wild reindeer.

What is special about reindeer?

Various sub-species of the wild boar can be found throughout Europe and Asia. All breeds of domestic pig originate from these species of wild boar. Specific breeding programmes have led to bizarre breeds such as the pot-bellied pig, the curly-tailed Mangalitza pig or unusual species like the black and white saddleback pig.

Are all domestic pigs descendants of the wild boar?

Horses are among the fastest runners of all the ungulates. Only the tips of their toes come into contact with the ground as their toes are protected by their hooves.

The mule is the result of crossing a male donkey with a female horse. It is used for riding and as a beast of burden.

How many species of mammal have been domesticated?

Out of a worldwide total of around 4,000 different species of mammal, 18 species have produced domestic animals such as cows and pigs whilst 15 species have been modified into pets, such as cats and dogs. In some cases, the line between pets and domestic animals is indistinct.

Which is the oldest type of domestic animal?

The dog is currently believed to be humanity's oldest domestic animal. The wolf was domesticated approximately 15,000 years ago, since which time the dog has been kept by humans. According to remains found in prehistoric settlements in Southeast Asia and believed to date back approximately 10,000 years, the next oldest domestic animals are sheep and goats. The pig was next to be domesticated around 9,000 to 9,500 years ago, then, roughly 8,500 years ago, man finally succeeded in domesticating wild cattle.

Do all domestic cattle originate from the same species?

They are believed to come from four main species. European cattle, as well as the zebu, are descendants of the extinct aurochs. The domesticated form of the Banteng ox is known as Bali cattle and the domestic yak is derived from the wild yak. Finally, the domesticated form of the wild gaur is the gayal.

Lamas are kept in semi-wild herds. They graze on the high grassy plains from the Peruvian Andes to northern Argentina up to altitudes of 4,000 metres.

Sheep, an undemanding species of grass-eating mammal, graze on the Halligen, a group of North Frisian islands, or on the coastal dyke. The lop-eared species living here are bred for their wool.

Zebus have lived in Asia for 6,500 years. They are adapted to cope well with relatively high temperatures.

The name refers to the hump on their shoulders, which contains powerful muscles and fatty tissue. Zebus are extremely well adapted to hot climates and are found in tropical and subtropical regions of Asia and Africa.

Why are zebus sometimes known as 'hump-backed cattle'?

This longhaired bovine is the domesticated form of the wild yak. Herds of wild yaks can be found throughout the Tibetan plateau at altitudes of up to 5,000 metres. Their thick coats protect them from the cold and their broad hooves prevent them from sinking into boggy ground. Tibetan people keep the smaller domestic yaks for their hair, milk and meat, and also as beasts of burden.

What is a yak?

The lama, a resilient beast of burden, and the alpaca, bred for its fleece, are both descended from the guanaco, a small member of the camel family found in South America. They were domesticated in pre-Colombian times. The lama has longer legs and is larger than the alpaca, which in turn has shorter legs than the guanaco. The lama remains an important means of transport in some of the remoter parts of the Andes.

Which domestic animals are descended from the guanaco?

This is an ancient species of sheep found primarily on the Lüneburg Heath in Germany. Heath sheep are bred mainly for their wool as they have a high proportion of downy hair. Their fleeces easily become matted. Both males and females of the species have horns.

What are heath sheep?

All domestic sheep are descended from the oriental wild sheep, particularly the mouflon, a subspecies of the wild sheep. Domestic sheep are divided into wool sheep and hair sheep. They provide meat, milk, wool and hide. They are gentle and easy animals to maintain.

What species was the ancestor of all breeds of domestic sheep?

Which mammal is the ancestor of the domestic goat?

All our domestic goats are descended from the Bezoar goat, which has a distribution ranging from the mountainous regions of Greece and some of the Aegean islands to Asia Minor, extending through Iraq and Iran, as far as Pakistan. Species of domestic goat found in Central Asia are descended from the markhor with its impressive, corkscrew-like horns.

From which animal is angora wool obtained?

Angora wool is obtained from rabbits, goats and cats. Angora animals are breeds of domestic animal, which are deliberately bred for their long hair. The name 'angora' is derived from the Turkish town of Ankara.

What do the sable, mink, racoon and chinchilla have in common?

All these animals have beautiful coats, which humans have coveted since time immemorial for the fur trade. Mammals such as the raccoon dog, the red fox and Arctic fox, and swamp beaver (nutria) have also been hunted for their fur. A dramatic drop in the populations of these animals living in the wild – the chinchilla, for example, is almost extinct in the wild – led to the large-scale breeding of these animals on fur farms. Several animals from certain species escaped from these farms and are now breeding in the wild.

Why is the civet kept as a domestic animal?

The African civet produces an odorous, greaselike secretion from glands below the tail, known as musk or civet. In its concentrated form, it gives off an unpleasant smell, but when diluted, it is a highly prized as an ingredient of expensive perfumes.

Which mammal is the domestic rabbit descended from?

The domestic rabbit is descended from its ancestor, the wild rabbit, from which it has inherited its relatively short ears and its habit of thumping its back feet on the ground when threatened.

Like their ancestors, domestic goats are most at home on steep mountain slopes. They are social animals and prefer to be among others of their kind.

The ferret is a domestic animal originally bred from the polecat. It was bred by the Romans who used it for hunting rabbits. Ferrets have become feral in Sardinia and Sicily.

Domestication is the process whereby animals become accustomed to being controlled by humans, who removed wild animals from their natural environment. They bred these animals for a specific use (food, clothing, and as beasts of burden, or for pets). They are distinguishable from wild animals by their modified shape, fur colour and behaviour. Compared to the original species, domesticated forms have brains which are 30 per cent smaller.

The Great Munsterlander was bred from medieval bird-hunting dogs for hunting purposes. It is a so-called 'pointer', that is to say, it lifts its front paw and adopts a pointing stance to signal that it has detected game.

A ferret is the domesticated form of the polecat. The colour of its fur can vary from natural polecat shades to cinnamon-coloured, Siamese-patterned or snow-white. White ferrets may have dark or red eyes, the latter being albinos. In hunting, ferrets are used to chase rabbits out of their burrows, a sport known as ferreting.

What is a ferret?

The dog has developed into over 400 different breeds, all of which are descended from the wolf. These range from the Chihuahua, the smallest breed of dog which stands just ankle high, to the Irish wolfhound, the tallest breed, which measures 80 centimetres high at the shoulder. Dogs vary widely not only in size but also in their coats. There are curly-haired dogs such as poodles, long- and short-haired dogs as well as hairless dogs like the Mexican hairless dog.

What domestic animal has developed into the widest variety of breeds?

The earliest recorded information on dogs was written by the Greek writer, Xenophon (approx. 430 to 350 B.C.). According to him, dogs were originally bred for hunting purposes. They can detect and flush out game or drive it out of its burrow. In addition, they can chase wild animals and retrieve game that has been brought down. They also serve as guard dogs protecting livestock from predators and can herd it in a given direction. Dogs are used to guard man's property or for pulling sleds. Only in more modern times have dogs been kept solely as pets and companions.

What purpose were dogs bred for?

Two breeds which, thanks to their intelligence, sturdiness, nature and build, are well suited to police work are the German shepherd and the Labrador retriever. Dogs have exceptionally sensitive hearing and sense of smell. They can search for missing persons or escaped prisoners and can sniff out drugs, explosives, bodies and weapons.

Which breeds of dog are best suited to police work?

Why do cats' eyes glow in the dark?

Cats have a reflective layer of tissue at the back of the eye, the tapetum lucidum, which reflects light back, thereby making even the smallest amount of light available to the photoreceptors and increasing the light passing through the eye. As a consequence, a cat's night vision is six times better than that of a human.

Why do cats not hurt themselves when they fall?

Cats will only land on their feet without injury if the drop is high enough. As they are falling, cats perform a clever twisting manoeuvre in mid-air in which their tail acts as a rudder. This mid-air twist is controlled by a balancing organ in the inner ear. Breeds of cat without tails, such as the Manx cat, would be seriously injured in such a fall.

Why does a Persian cat require so much grooming?

Persian cats have the longest fur and thickest undercoat of any domestic cat. The upper layer of hair can grow to 12 or 15 centimetres in length. Daily brushing and combing prevents the hair matting and becoming tangled. It also removes hairs which the cat would otherwise swallow when grooming itself. In the case of Persian cats, this can lead to constipation, or even intestinal blockages.

Persian cats are pedigree cats and must conform to specific breeding regulations. They must have a large, round head with a wide skull and round face. They have a little button nose and a distinctive dent between the forehead and nose.

We repeatedly hear or read of cats travelling considerable distances in order to find their way back to their owners. How they do this over distances of 500 kilometres or more is a mystery. In the case of distances of up to five kilometres, it is believed that cats find their way home by relying on their visual memory and a sound map of their surroundings (recognisable sounds such as church bells, nature sounds, or specific animal noises).

Is there any truth in the claim that cats have a homing instinct?

What may appear cruel to humans is actually natural and necessary behaviour on the part of a cat. The business of hunting is hugely stressful and the cat cannot begin eating its prey until it has had time to relax. It does so by playing with its victim, for example, by allowing it to escape and then catching it again.

Why do cats play with their prey?

A mature female cat comes into season twice or three times a year. During this time, she will roam restlessly around the house, calling for a mate and rolling around on the floor. These are all signs that she is 'in heat'.

What does it mean when a cat is said to be 'in heat'?

Kittens are born blind and deaf after a gestation period averaging 63 days. They open their eyes during the second week and at the age of three weeks begin to explore their surroundings. They can eat solid food from the fourth week.

All cats love mice. They practise and perfect the process of catching a rodent during games with their siblings.

What mammal is known as the 'Indian pig'?

The guinea pig is known in some languages as the 'Indian pig'. The first guinea pigs were introduced to Europe in 1540 by the Spaniards after the discovery of South America by Colombus. At the time, people believed this continent to be India, hence the name 'Indian pig'. Dutch traders brought more guinea pigs back from South America around 1670 as gifts for their children.

Guinea pigs are delightful little creatures which are very popular as children's pets as they can become very tame, love being stroked, can be fed and do not scratch or bite.

How many breeds have descended from the domesticated rabbit?

Selective breeding has produced over 100 different breeds of domestic rabbit, which vary widely in fur colour and markings. All normal-sized rabbits as well as dwarf varieties are available in the full range of fur colours. White rabbits are known as Dutch rabbits, all other shades are grouped together as coloured rabbits. White rabbits can have blue or red eyes (albinos). Rabbits with pendulous ears are known as lop-eared rabbits and were first developed in 1952.

What is a degu?

The degu is a small rodent belonging to the octodon group. These social, diurnal creatures occur in Central Chile and are found up to altitudes of 3,000 metres in the Andes. If kept as a pet, the degu requires hiding places in its cage to replicate its underground habitat.

In addition to the natural colour of the original species, numerous fur shades and types of coat have been developed from the Syrian golden hamster. These include hamsters with checkered markings, beige and white hamsters with dark ears (Russian hamsters), Teddy bear hamsters with luxuriant fur and long-haired hamsters.

The house mouse came to Europe from Japan in the mid-19th century as a tame laboratory mouse. Millions of mice are subjected to experimentation for medical or research purposes and many die during the process.

Why are hamsters sometimes unsuitable as pets?

Hamsters, such as the golden hamster are active at dusk and during the night and spend their days sleeping. However, for anyone who is busy during the day and only has time for a pet in the evening, a golden hamster is the perfect solution for it is then that the hamster is most active and displays its true nature.

Which is the best place to buy a pet?

It is best to go to a breeder who specialises in the type of animal required, or to pet shops, which occasionally also look after animals while their owners are away on holiday.

The first chinchilla pelts were brought to Europe after the Spanish conquest of South America. The thick, light fur was highly prized and the pelts made into coats and jackets. It takes at least 100 pelts to make a coat. Since only rich people could afford this type of coat, hunting chinchillas became a lucrative business. As a consequence, the chinchilla population in the wild was so decimated that people began breeding them on fur farms. It is only recently that chinchillas have become popular as pets.

Albino varieties of the mouse and brown rat are used in laboratories for medical and biological research, hence the expression 'laboratory animals'. White mice and rats have evolved due to a lack of pigmentation caused by a genetic change. White rats are much less aggressive than their wild cousins and are easy to breed.

How did the chinchilla reach Europe?

What are laboratory animals?

Which mammal is the emblem of a major environmental organisation?

The giant panda is the emblem of the World Wildlife Fund for Nature (WWF). This mammal was once widespread throughout China but nowadays there are only a few animals left in three Chinese provinces along the eastern edge of the Tibetan plateau. Its appealing appearance and endangered status make it the perfect logo for the WWF.

What can be done to save the giant panda?

There are thought to be only around 1,000 pandas left in the wild. Their dwindling numbers are due to loss of their natural habitat as bamboo forests are converted into agricultural land. The panda feeds almost entirely on bamboo shoots. Although it is a protected species in China, the panda will only be saved if the destruction of its habitat is halted.

Why is the Iberian lynx under threat?

The Iberian lynx is native to the Iberian Peninsula and is most common in areas with high wild rabbit populations. For some time now, reforestation projects in Spain have been causing a decline in the number of rabbits since these mammals cannot survive in a forest environment. As a result, the Iberian lynx is losing its supply of natural prey and has become extremely endangered. There are now fewer than 100 lynxes left in the wild.

With its long, silkily soft fur, patterned with large dark rosettes of colour on a light background, the snow leopard or irbis is one of the most beautiful cats in the world.

Like many other big cats, the snow leopard has been heavily hunted for its beautifully patterned, thick fur. Although hunting has been banned in the countries it inhabits and the species is now strictly protected, the smuggling trade in snow leopard furs continues to flourish as poachers can make a great deal of money from them. Only a few hundred of these animals remain in the wild.

What has been the snow leopard's undoing?

When Père David's deer, or the Milu, first became known in Europe, there were scarcely any of them left in the wild in their native China. Two hundred of these majestic animals lived in a park, some of which were brought to European zoos. This was fortunate as many of the deer drowned in floods and the remainder died during the Boxer rebellion. The species therefore became extinct in the wild. Père David's deer have reproduced successfully in zoos and plans are in hand in China to release some of these deer back into the wild.

What species of deer is now only found in zoos and parks?

The entire world population of the Javan rhinoceros is now just 60 animals. They live in a small area in the western part of Java. These forest-dwellers are distinguished by the armour plating on their shoulders and by their single horn.

How many Javan rhinoceroses are left in the world?

The giant panda is the emblem of the WWF, a worldwide environmental protection agency. This popular animal with its striking black and white colouring and appealing appearance is a great favourite with people and as such makes the perfect emblem for wildlife protection.

The Javan and Sumatran rhinoceroses are classed as forest rhinoceroses. They inhabit the rainforests of Southeast Asia. The Javan rhinoceros is now confined to the island of Java.

Why was the goral hunted?

As protection against the cold, the goral has a thick, warm coat. Its meat is also highly prized. What is more, the heart, horns and embryos of this chamois-type mammal also play a major role in traditional East Asian medicine. As a result, the goral was so heavily hunted that by 1924, when it was made a protected species, three-quarters of its population had been exterminated. The remaining population is now estimated at around 600.

Which species of pig is one of the ten most endangered species in the world?

The pygmy hog was once widespread from southwest Nepal to northeast India (Assam) where it fed on elephant grass. Nowadays, it is confined to a single protected population in a national park in northwest Assam. Its dramatic decline is a result of the dwindling supply of elephant grass and the conversion of land to agriculture. They were also hunted for their meat.

Which New World monkey is one of the most endangered?

There are only 1,000 muriquis, or woolly spider monkeys, still surviving in the southeastern corner of Brazil. The destruction of their mountain forests has brought the muriqui, the largest species of South American monkey, to the brink of extinction. Only an urgent rescue programme can save this species.

The wanderoo or lion-tailed macaque has a fine mane of light-coloured hair surrounding its dark face. This animal has been heavily hunted for its meat.

Mountain gorillas are peaceful herbivores and found only in three small areas of Uganda, Rwanda and Zaire.

In appearance, the goral resembles a domestic goat, which is why it is classed as a goat-antelope. Elastic horn pads underneath its hooves make it extremely sure-footed on rocky hillsides where it seeks refuge from predators.

The wanderoo lives in the forested mountain regions of southwest India. The destruction of its habitat and the fact that it has been hunted for its skin have reduced the surviving numbers of this mammal to just a few hundred. It is also hunted by the local population for its pleasant-tasting meat.

Why is the wanderoo listed in the Washington Convention on International Trade in Endangered Species of Wild Fauna and Flora?

The mountain gorilla is threatened, not just by hunters and poachers and the destruction of its habitat, but also by visiting tourists. They carry diseases with them against which gorillas have no immunity. The number of gorillas left in the wild is now as low as 200 or 300 animals.

Which primate is listed as being critically endangered?

This is an official list of endangered species of a country's flora and fauna. This systematic listing forms the basis for regulations and laws aimed at protecting the species. These lists are updated at regular intervals.

What is meant by the 'Red List'?

This is an international agreement signed in 1973 by a large number of states, which aims to limit the trade in endangered species of wild animals and plants, as well as in animal-based products. The endangered species are listed in appendices and placed in order of vulnerability. Appendix I species are on the point of extinction, Appendix II varieties are classed as potentially endangered and Appendix III species are protected in their native land.

What is the Washington Convention on International Trade in Endangered Species of Wild Fauna and Flora?

The koala, a marsupial, was once found all over Australia. They have been so decimated by forest fires, epidemics and hunting, that koalas are now only found in the eastern part of the country. The koala has been a protected species since 1930.

What animal is the emblem of Australia?

Picture credits: MEV (30), Miles Kelly Art Library (32), OKAPIA (113); Cover design: Getty.